Geology of the country around Bude and Bradworthy

Bude is a popular holiday resort close to some of the few sandy beaches of the Atlantic coast of north Cornwall and west Devon. A majestic cliff line rises northwards, broken by a handful of small bays where short swift streams cascade into the sea. Many observers will see only the interplay of sand and rock, bright sun-reflecting water and deep cliff-cast shadow. But to the few these cliffs hold the key to much of the Upper Carboniferous stratigraphy of south-west England.

This book unravels the structure of the coast and projects it inland, where the evidence is sparse. For the tourist there is description of a magnificent shoreline with more cliff waterfalls than any comparable stretch in Britain, and speculation about the Devil's Stone at Shebbear—does it belong, or was it brought by pious Celt or Pleistocene ice? For the scientist there is pure geology. For the planner there is an interpretation of the countryside of Sutcombe and Sheepwash, Bradworthy and Buckland Brewer, an area beyond the pressures of industry and urban spread, of few natural resources or rich soils, where there is still time to comprehend the landscape and realise its potential.

Plate 1   Box fold in Bude Formation, Dunsmouth

An almost symmetrical box fold in sandstones, siltstones and mudstones shows a small subsidiary crumple on its north (left) flank. (A 12065).

GEOLOGICAL SURVEY OF GREAT BRITAIN

England and Wales

E. C. FRESHNEY

E. A. EDMONDS

R. T. TAYLOR and

B. J. WILLIAMS

CONTRIBUTOR

R. J. Merriman

Geology of the country around Bude and Bradworthy

Memoir for 1:50 000 geological sheets 307 and 308

INSTITUTE OF GEOLOGICAL SCIENCES

Natural Environment Research Council

LONDON HER MAJESTY'S STATIONERY OFFICE 1979

Bibliographical reference

FRESHNEY, E. C., EDMONDS, E. A., TAYLOR, R. T. and
WILLIAMS, B. J. 1979.
Geology of the country around Bude and Bradworthy.
Mem. Geol. Surv. G.B., Sheets 307 and 308.

Authors and Contributor

E. C. FRESHNEY, BSc, PhD, E. A. EDMONDS, MSc,
R. T. TAYLOR, BSc, PhD and B. J. WILLIAMS, BSc
Institute of Geological Sciences, St Just,
30 Pennsylvania Road, Exeter EX4 6BX

R. J. Merriman, BSc
Institute of Geological Sciences, London

Other publications of the Institute dealing with this and
adjoining districts.

BOOKS

British Regional Geology
South-West England, 4th Edition, 1975

Memoirs
Geology of the country around Okehampton, 1968
Geology of the country around Boscastle and Holsworthy,
1972
Geology of the country around Bideford and Lundy
Island, 1979
Geology of the country around Chulmleigh, 1979

Mineral Dossier
Ball Clay, 1975

MAPS

1:625 000
Sheet 2 Geological
Sheet 2 Quaternary
Sheet 2 Aeromagnetic

1:1 584 000
Tectonic map of Great Britain and Northern Ireland

1:50 000
Sheet 292 and others (Bideford and Lundy) 1977
Sheet 307 and 308 (Bude and Bradworthy) (in press)
Sheet 309 (Chulmleigh) (in press)
Sheet 310 (Tiverton) 1969
Sheet 323 (Holsworthy) 1974
Sheet 324 (Okehampton) 1969

1:250 000 (Diagram Edition of Aeromagnetic Map)
Sheet 1 South-Western Approaches
Sheet 2 Southern England and English Channel

Typeset for the Institute of Geological Sciences by Raithby,
Lawrence & Company Ltd, Leicester and London

Illustration films by U. D. O. Jenn Ltd, London

Printed in England for Her Majesty's Stationery Office by
Staples Printers St Albans Limited at The Priory Press

Dd 596477 K16

ISBN 0 11 884117 3

PREFACE

The account of the geology of the Bude district (Sheet 308) is presented along with that of Bude Bay (Sheet 307), the narrow coastal strip on the western margin of the district. The northern part of the area of Sheet 308 has been described in detail in the Bideford and Lundy Island Memoir, and this area around the southern coast of Bideford Bay is reproduced on both the Bideford (292) and Bude (308) 1:50 000 New Series Geological Sheets.

Apart from a small Tertiary outlier in the north-eastern part of the district, the solid rocks are all of Upper Carboniferous age. Their structure and stratigraphy are interpreted in the light of evidence gathered from the excellent Atlantic coastal section, and the coastal sections of adjacent sheets.

The area was first surveyed geologically by Sir Henry T. De La Beche in the years between 1835 and 1839, and published on Old Series sheets 26 and 29. The main part of the six-inch geological survey was carried out in the years 1970 to 1973, with marginal areas of overlap from adjacent sheets being mapped between 1964 and 1969. The mapping was done by Dr E. C. Freshney, Mr B. J. Williams, Mr E. A. Edmonds, Dr R. T. Taylor and Mr D. Patrick, with small areas by Mr K. E. Beer and the late Dr M. Williams, under Mr G. Bisson as District Geologist. Fossils were collected by Mr D. E. Butler, Dr D. E. White and the surveyors, and identified by Dr M. A. Calver and Dr W. H. C. Ramsbottom. An account of the petrography of some Carboniferous rocks has been contributed by Mr R. J. Merriman. Photographs listed in Appendix 2 were taken by Mr J. Rhodes and Mr C. Jeffery. An account of regional geophysical investigations covering the district is included in the Bideford and Lundy Island Memoir.

The 1:50 000 geological map which this memoir describes is in press. In adjacent districts One-Inch Sheet 322 (Boscastle) was published in 1969, 1:50 000 Sheet 323 (Holsworthy) was published in 1974, and 1:50 000 Sheet 292 (Bideford) was published in 1977. The memoir was compiled by Mr Williams and edited by Mr Edmonds.

AUSTIN W. WOODLAND
Director

Institute of Geological Sciences
Exhibition Road
South Kensington
London SW7 2DE
26 March 1979

LIST OF SIX-INCH MAPS

The following is a list of six-inch National Grid maps included, wholly or in part, in Sheets 307 and 308, with the dates of survey. The officers are: K. E. Beer, E. A. Edmonds, E. C. Freshney, D. Patrick, R. T. Taylor, B. J. Williams and M. Williams.

Manuscript copies of the six-inch maps are available for public reference in the library of the Institute of Geological Sciences.

SS 20 NW & 10 NE	Bude Freshney, Patrick and M. Williams	1963–70
SS 20 NE	Grimscott Freshney and M. Williams	1963–70
SS 21 SW & 11 SE	Cleave Camp Freshney	1971–72
SS 21 SE	Kilkhampton Freshney	1971–72
SS 21 NW & 11 NE	Morwenstow Freshney	1971
SS 21 NE	Meddon Freshney	1971
SS 22 SW	Hartland Quay Taylor	1969–70
SS 22 SE	Hartland Taylor	1969–70
SS 22 NE	Beckland Taylor	1969
SS 30 NW	Chilsworthy Edmonds and M. Williams	1964–72
SS 30 NE	Thornbury Edmonds and M. Williams	1966–72
SS 31 SW	Bradworthy Edmonds	1973
SS 31 SE	Abbots Bickington Edmonds and B. J. Williams	1973
SS 31 NW	Ashmansworthy Freshney	1972–73
SS 31 NE	East Putford B. J. Williams	1972–73
SS 32 SW	Clovelly Taylor and B. J. Williams	1969–72
SS 32 SE	Buck's Mills B. J. Williams	1969–71
SS 32 NW	Hartland Point Taylor	1968–69
SS 40 NW	Shebbear Edmonds	1966–72
SS 40 NE	Sheepwash Edmonds, Freshney and Beer	1965–72
SS 41 SW	Newton St Petrock B. J. Williams	1972–73
SS 41 SE	Peters Marland B. J. Williams and Freshney	1966–73
SS 41 NW	Tythecott B. J. Williams	1972
SS 41 NE	Little Torrington B. J. Williams and Freshney	1967–72
SS 42 SW	Littleham B. J. Williams	1969–71
SS 42 SE	Landcross B. J. Williams and Freshney	1968–71

CONTENTS

PLATES

FIGURES

TABLE

GEOLOGICAL SUCCESSION

SUPERFICIAL DEPOSITS (Drift)

Recent and Pleistocene

Landslip	Collapsed strata of cliff tops
Blown sand	Dune sand
Alluvium	Silts, clays and gravels
River terraces	Mainly silts
Marine beach deposits	Sands, shingle and boulders
Head	Stony and sandy clay

SOLID FORMATIONS		*Generalised thickness* m
? Eocene	Flint gravels	?50
Permian		
Bow Conglomerates	Breccio-conglomerates	98
Upper Carboniferous		
Bude Formation (Westphalian)	Thick-bedded and massive sandstones with siltstones and shales	1290
Crackington Formation (Namurian and Westphalian)	Shales with turbidite sandstones	340

NOTES

National Grid references are given in square brackets
throughout the memoir. All lie within the 100-km square SS.
Numbers preceded by A refer to photographs in the
Institute's collections.
Letters preceding specimen numbers refer to Institute
collections as follows:
E   English sliced rocks
DX   X-ray diffractometer charts
The authorship of fossil species is given in Appendix 1.

CHAPTER 1

Introduction

GEOGRAPHY AND PHYSIOGRAPHY

This book describes the geology of the northernmost tip of Cornwall and an adjacent area of north-west Devon (Figure 1). Bude lies in the south-west corner of the district, Bideford Bay to the north and Torrington on the eastern edge.

The monthly mean temperature at Bude ranges from 42.6°F (6.6°C) in February to 60.4°F (17.7°C) in August. June is the sunniest month, with an average of 222 hours of bright sunshine out of an annual figure of 1629 hours. Rainfall is about 40 inches (1016 mm) a year at Bude, increasing to the north and east to 55 inches (1397 mm) just south of Bideford Bay and 45 inches (1143 mm) towards Torrington. Frosts are rarely severe on the coast, but sea mists are common.

The Upper Carboniferous rocks which underlie the district are strikingly exposed along most of the coast, in cliffs rising 100 m and more and in buttresses picked out by differential erosion. A 60-m marine platform is developed around Bude, and the lower cliffs thereabouts border the only extensive areas of beach sand and blown sand in the district.

Inland high land at 200 to 220 m OD borders the headwater streams of the River Torridge to the east and west of Woolfardisworthy and to the north and west of Bradworthy. The countryside is slightly more varied in the north of the district than in the south, with fairly deeply incised valleys cutting the higher ground and rapidly flowing streams traversing thin oak woodlands. The main watershed runs south-south-eastwards from near Youlstone [276 157] to Holsworthy Beacon. To the east of it drainage is southerly and easterly to the River Torridge, to the west lie the southerly-flowing headwaters of the River Tamar. All around the coast short fast-running streams hurry seawards, but their erosive power cannot keep pace with that of the Atlantic breakers and several disgorge from hanging valleys high above the beach. Little Water, 3 km N of Bude, falls over 20 m.

The north-west corner of the district has been designated an Area of Outstanding Natural Beauty, and the Torridge Valley near Torrington has great charm. Elsewhere the inland landscape is unpretentious, and scenic grandeur is confined to the coast.

MAN AND INDUSTRY

Clovelly Dykes [311 235] is an Iron Age earthwork with concentric ramparts, a type largely confined to South Wales and south-west England, more a defendable cattle pound than a major hill fort. A similar structure occurs at Embury [218 196], and other Iron Age earthworks, with single walls, at Windbury [287 267], Peppercombe Castle [378 240] and Hembury Castle [427 179]. Apart from a few flint artefacts found scattered at Hartland and elsewhere, these structures are the earliest evidence of man within the district. Part of the religious beliefs of the Celtic people who created the earthworks was veneration for old stones, and it seems likely that the 'Devil's Stone' at Shebbear (pp. 48–49) first acquired its significance in connection with the Celtic New Year at the beginning of November, an ominous time when all supernatural powers were thought to be abroad. There is little evidence of Roman occupation. Monastic remains occur at Hartland Abbey [240 248], Frithelstock [463 195] and possibly Clovelly [309 251].

Human activity in the district has remained founded on agriculture since Mesolithic times, and the impact of the twentieth century tourist boom, away from the immediate vicinity of Bude, has been less than in most other coastal areas of the south-west. Thin clayey, silty and fine sandy soils are characteristically developed and support dairy and stock farming. Arable land is less common, except on some of the slightly coarser sandy soils in the south, inland from Bude, and in the north towards Bideford. Poor wet acid soils of the high ground carry blocks of commercial forestry plantings which together constitute Hartland Forest. In the main they comprise stands of those species, mostly spruces, best able to yield a first crop in exposed situations. It seems possible that later crops might include more pines and Douglas Firs. Further afforestation is probable; forestry represents a use of land well-suited to the position, the climate and the soils, and increased plantings will surely occur if the economics of the industry permit.

There was a trial digging for copper near Hartland in the nineteenth century, but otherwise the only mining near the district has been of the 'Bideford Black'. This seam of 'culm' crops out on the coast at Greencliff and trends inland through Bideford. It was worked first as a fuel, later as a pigment. Many small quarries have been opened in Carboniferous sandstones, mainly for local use in farm buildings, walls and roads. A few have supplied stone farther afield. Colpit Quarry [2795 2392] near Hartland is still active, as is the Braunton Sand Company's Beam Quarry [471 204] near Great Torrington, but Bradworthy Mill Quarry [3180 1435] is currently closed. Sandstone was recently quarried for use in the small new dam [290 117] near Kilkhampton.

Bude (pop. with Stratton 5280) is a popular holiday resort and small port located where the several streams which coalesce on the 60-m marine platform emerge at the coast in Bude Haven. It is also the terminus of the Bude Canal, along which shelly beach sand was carried inland for use as manure during most of the nineteenth century.

Great Torrington (pop. 3010), standing high above the meandering River Torridge, developed from a small market town into a minor centre for the manufacture of dairy products and gloves. More recently a factory producing

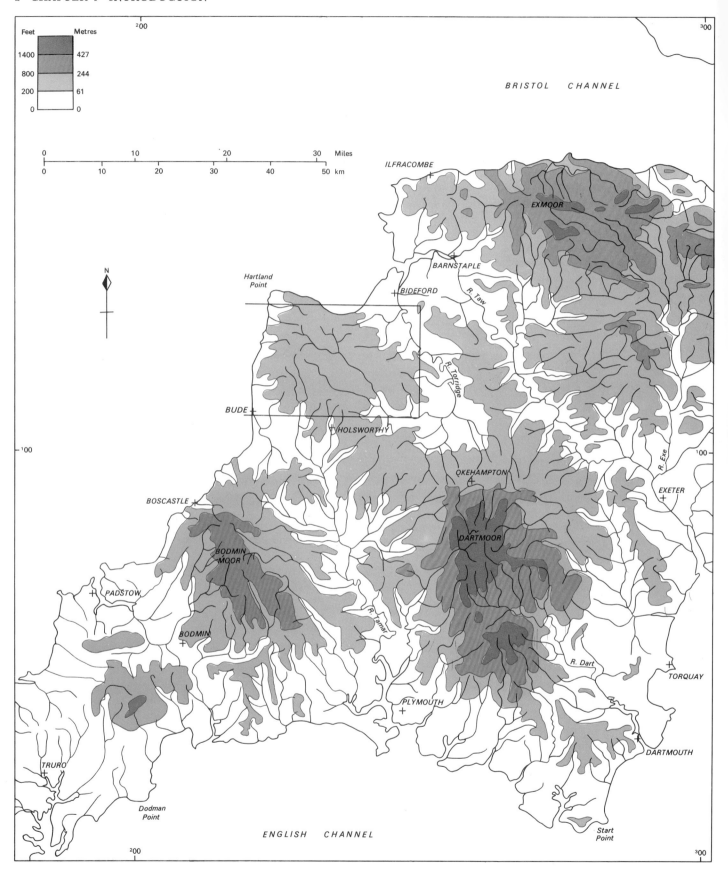

Figure 1 Sketch-map showing the position of the Bude district

high-quality glassware has been established in the town by a Swedish parent company.

Bideford (pop. 11 000), to the north-east of the district, carries on a reduced sea-borne trade and is the main commercial centre, although a small one.

Communications are poor. The northern branch of the Bude Canal lay mainly within the present district and terminated at Alfardisworthy. It was fed by water from a small reservoir there, now called Tamar Lake, and now forms an aqueduct supplying water to Bude and Stratton. The canal, however, has long been closed, as has the Rolle Canal from Bideford to Torrington. Railways have never penetrated the district beyond its southern and eastern margins. That through Holsworthy to Bude is now dismantled, and although a line from Meeth past Torrington to Bideford and Barnstaple remains in use it carries only freight. Bus services are few, and an area never very easy of access has become less so, except to the private motorist.

Water resources consist of surface supplies, except for the many small wells serving remote farms and cottages. Most of the district is underlain by Carboniferous sandstones of such fine-grained texture that movement of groundwater through them is extremely slow. Some coarser sandstones occur in the south and in the north, but are of such limited extent and capacity as to constitute only minor aquifers offering no prospect of large supplies. Similarly there are no large resources available in drift deposits.

The area described in this memoir exhibits no clear development trend to project into the future. There is no large centre of population, although some varied employment at the margins of the district is provided by the small towns of Bude, Holsworthy, Torrington and Bideford. Elsewhere, it seems that *laissez-faire* evolution will lead only to economic decline, dictated by a combination of remoteness and lack of natural resources, and alleviated but not halted by the small seasonal tourist trade.

GEOLOGICAL HISTORY

Shales and fine-grained turbidite sandstones of the Crackington Formation, the oldest rocks exposed in the district, probably originated in moderately deep water which remained generally undisturbed except by occasional turbid sediment-laden currents flowing down the submarine slopes. The overlying Bude Formation comprises shales and fine-grained sandstones, which are locally massive and typically show little internal structure. Perhaps these sediments accumulated in shallower water.

At the close of Carboniferous times all these sediments were caught up in the earth movements of the Variscan orogeny, crumpled into folds aligned approximately east–west, and locally fractured by strike faults. Such folding is well displayed in the cliffs between Bude and Hartland Point.

Sparse but widely scattered debris indicates that an extensive cover of rudaceous sediments formed in the desert regime of the succeeding Permian period, but all that survives is the small outlier of red breccio-conglomerates at Portledge.

The Alpine orogeny of mid-Tertiary times produced many NW-trending faults in south-west England, of which one of the largest, the Sticklepath Fault, cuts the coast near Greencliff just north of the present district. Movement on these same lines of fracture may have occurred both earlier and later. A small patch of Tertiary gravel occurs at Orleigh Court.

There is no conclusive evidence of the district ever having been overridden by an ice sheet. Ice crossed the Bristol Channel, pressed against the cliffs, penetrated short distances up some estuaries and disrupted the coastal drainage pattern during the penultimate (Wolstonian) glaciation. Possible ice-diverted drainage channels occur near Clovelly. Boulders at and near Shebbear, including the famous Devil's Stone, could be relics of an ancient more extensive ice sheet but afford no proof (p. 49).

The youngest terrace of the River Torridge probably dates from the final (Ipswichian) interglacial period.

During the last (Devensian) glaciation, the southernmost ice front reached South Wales. Much Head formed in the district, as it did over much of the rest of south-west England, during the annual freeze-thaw cycles of the periglacial regions peripheral to the ice-cap.

PREVIOUS RESEARCH

De la Beche's classic *Report on the geology of Cornwall, Devon and West Somerset* (1839) was preceded by his notes on the 'culm' of Bideford (1835), and by early work by Conybeare (1814, 1823) at Clovelly. Sedgwick and Murchison subsequently (1840) made a major contribution to the geology of the south-west which permitted De la Beche's 'Grauwacke' to be divided into Devonian and Carbonaceous Series (or Carboniferous). Etheridge (1867) made structural studies of general relevance to the Bude district.

Ussher's great resurvey resulted in a number of papers (1881, 1887, 1892, 1900, 1901), and he published a coloured geological map in the Devonshire volume of the Victoria History of the Counties of England (1906).

Arber (1907, 1911) discussed Upper Carboniferous strata and the geology and physiography of the north Devon coast, and Rogers (1907, 1908, 1909, 1910) the Carboniferous fossils of the region. For many years a map published to accompany an excursion report by Hamling and Rogers (1910) remained the most detailed geological map of north Devon; it owed much to Ussher.

More recently Carboniferous stratigraphy and structure have been investigated by Prentice (1960), De Raaf, Reading and Walker (1965), Reading (1965) and Freshney and Taylor (1971, 1972), and reviewed by House and Selwood (1966) and Edmonds (1974).

The geology of north Devon was summarised within a regional framework by Edmonds, McKeown and Williams (1975). **EAE**

CHAPTER 2
Upper Carboniferous

GENERAL ACCOUNT

The Upper Carboniferous of the Bude district consists mainly of Bude Formation, which includes the Greencliff Beds of Prentice (1960), part of his Cockington Beds, Ussher's Morchard-type Culm or Middle Culm and some of his Eggesford-type Culm (Ussher, 1906). The Welcombe Measures (Ashwin, 1958), the main part of Ussher's Eggesford-type Culm and some of the Cockington Beds, which were all once thought to overlie the Bude Formation, have been shown to underlie it (Freshney and Taylor, 1972) and to correlate with the top part of the Crackington Formation on the southern side of the synclinorium (Edmonds and others, 1968, p. 52; Freshney, McKeown and Williams, 1972, p. 36). In coastal exposures (Figure 2) between Embury and Marsland, a complete succession can be seen passing up from Namurian beds below the Embury Shale (*Gastrioceras subcrenatum* horizon) through strata equivalent to the Wanson Beds of Mackintosh (1965) to the Gull Rock Shale (*Gastrioceras listeri* horizon). The succeeding beds are turbiditic sandstones and shales similar to those described as transitional or passage beds in the Okehampton and Boscastle memoirs, and the top of the Crackington Formation on the Hartland coast may be taken at the top of the Hartland Quay Shale (*Gastrioceras amaliae* horizon). In practice the boundary mapped is the base of the lowest of the massive sandstones characteristic of the Bude Formation and is to some extent diachronous. The Bude Formation youngs generally if irregularly southwards towards the synclinorial axis near Duckpool, where the youngest Westphalian strata known in south-west England occur, the Warren Gutter Shale being correlated with the '*Anthracoceras*' *aegiranum* horizon. Thus the formation as described here extends some 820 m above the Saturday's Pit Shale, which was suggested as the top of the Bude Formation by King (1971), and some 70 m below the slumped bed which King suggested as the base in his faulted succession.

The outcrop pattern of the Upper Carboniferous formations reflects the presence of large east–west anticlinoria and synclinoria. The greater part of the district is underlain by Bude Formation occupying a synclinorial trough, the axis of which runs from Duckpool on the coast to Buckland Filleigh in the east. A small tract of Crackington Formation strata lies on the southern flank of the structure near Sheepwash. An anticlinorium in the north with its axis through Embury Beach brings up Crackington Formation, but the fold plunges eastwards and these older rocks pass beneath Bude Formation south-west of Parkham. A complementary synclinorium to the north contains Bude Formation rocks which crop out south of Speke's Mill Mouth on the coast and also inland south-east of Clovelly. Crackington Formation south of Hartland may reflect variation in the plunge of the synclinorium, but exposure in this area is poor. In the north-east the Crackington Formation is truncated to the north by a major east–west fault beyond which Bude Formation crops out (Edmonds, Williams and Taylor, 1979).

CRACKINGTON FORMATION

The largest outcrop of Crackington Formation in the district, around and south of Hartland, consists predominantly of fine-grained greyish green turbiditic sandstones usually between 0.3 and 1 m thick. The sandstones are sharply defined at top and bottom, and are characterised by sedimentary structures such as groove-casts, flute-casts and bounce-casts which indicate derivation mainly from around west-south-west but partly from between north-west and south-west. They show poor grading and in some cases lamination and cross-lamination at their tops.

Shales and mudstones occur mostly as partings less than 0.3 m thick, and the sandstone to shale ratio is commonly around 3:1. The thickest argillaceous sequence occurs between the Embury Shale and the Gull Rock Shale (Freshney and Taylor, 1972) and comprises about 70 m of shales with many thin sandstones (Plate 2); the latter carry small sole-structures, of which the bounce-casts are commonly rich in goniatite debris. The position of this shaly sequence, which is closely comparable to the Wanson Beds of Mackintosh (1965), is shown in Figure 3; a 6-m slumped bed occurs at the top. Other shaly successions occur with bases 200 and 223 m above the Embury Shale, the higher one being thin and containing some ironstone bands. The most important shale bands, however, are the Embury Shale and the Gull Rock Shale, containing faunas indicative of the *Gastrioceras subcrenatum* horizon and the *Gastrioceras listeri* horizon respectively. They differ from the other shales and mudstones within the main part of the sequence in being much darker grey and in containing abundant pyrite and bands of calcareous nodules; in the Gull Rock Shale these nodules coalesce locally into a limestone band.　ECF

The upper part of the Crackington Formation is repeated to the north of the Embury anticlinorium. The Gull Rock Shale is exposed at Gull Rock Beach [2144 2001], and reappears in a group of anticlines in the cliff and on the foreshore between Elmscott Gutter [2228 2155] and Mansley Beach [2220 2208].

The Hartland Quay Shale, yielding *G. amaliae* and recognised at Litter Mouth, forms a prominent marker horizon near the top of the Crackington Formation. Freshney and Taylor (1972) suggested the base of this shale as the Crackington Formation–Bude Formation junction on the coast. However, subsequent work has located a thin shale band with *G. amaliae* 3 m below the main shale band at Sandhole Rock and 4.7 m below it at Hole Rock. This lower shale band is poorly developed at Hartland Quay [2242 2485] and Cow and Calf [2283 2720] (Edmonds, Williams and Taylor, 1979) and has not been found beneath the

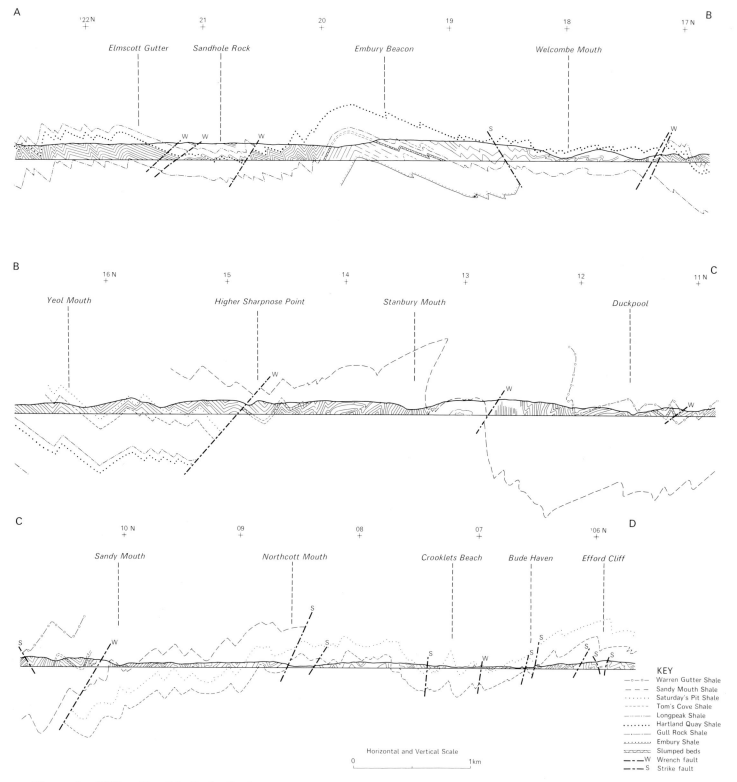

Figure 2 Cliff profile of the Bude district

KEY

—o—o— Warren Gutter Shale
– – – Sandy Mouth Shale
········ Saturday's Pit Shale
– – – – Tom's Cove Shale
–·–·– Longpeak Shale
●●●● Hartland Quay Shale
–··–··– Gull Rock Shale
········· Embury Shale
∿∿∿∿ Slumped beds
—·—W Wrench fault
—·—S Strike fault

Horizontal and Vertical Scale
0   1km

Figure 3   Generalised vertical sections
of parts of the coast between Brownspear
Beach [224 235] and Duckpool showing
the correlation of the nodular shales

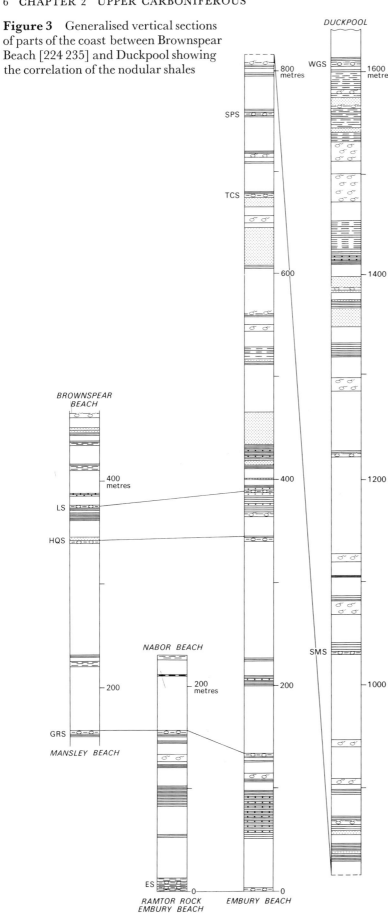

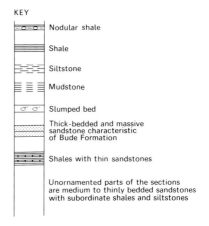

KEY

Nodular shale

Shale

Siltstone

Mudstone

Slumped bed

Thick-bedded and massive
sandstone characteristic
of Bude Formation

Shales with thin sandstones

Unornamented parts of the sections
are medium to thinly bedded sandstones
with subordinate shales and siltstones

WGS   Warren Gutter Shale
       'Anthracoceras' aegiranum horizon

SMS   Sandy Mouth Shale

SPS   Saturday's Pit Shale

TCS   Tom's Cove Shale

LS   Longpeak Shale

HQS   Hartland Quay Shale
       Gastrioceras amaliae horizon

GRS   Gull Rock Shale
       Gastrioceras listeri horizon

ES   Embury Shale
       Gastrioceras subcrenatum horizon

Plate 2   Crumpled shales with thin sandstones of the Crackington Formation, Embury Beach

Pyritous shales and thin turbiditic sandstones between the Embury Shale and the Gull Rock Shale show intense crumpling, reflecting both their position in the steep limb of the Embury anticlinorium and their relative incompetence in comparison with strata above and below. A fracture cleavage is well developed parallel to the axial planes of the crumples. (A 12467).

Hartland Quay Shale east of Hartland Point. The whole of the Hartland Quay Shale is, therefore, best included in the Crackington Formation. The thickness of the formation between the Embury Shale and the Hartland Quay Shale to the north of the Embury anticlinorium is about 340 m.

In an anticline at Skittering Rock [3175 2507] north-west of Clovelly, a nodular shale corresponding to the Namurian *G. cancellatum* horizon has been located just north of the present district. The extension of this Namurian succession to the north-west has been described by Edmonds, Williams and Taylor (1979). The continuation of the succession to the south-east is poorly exposed and appears to be cut out by faults near Clovelly.   RTT

The Crackington Formation in the north-east part of the district, around Landcross, comprises the more sandstone-rich strata from the Gull Rock Shale upwards to the base of the Bude Formation; the lower beds have been cut out by the major east–west normal fault which reintroduces Bude Formation to the north.   BJW

In the south-eastern corner of the district the topmost Crackington Formation strata comprise greenish grey and brown shales and silty shales with scattered beds of fine-grained silty sandstone generally less than 0.3 m thick. These sandstones include fewer recognisable turbidites than is typical of the formation, and similar beds in the extreme north-western corner of the Okehampton district (Edmonds and others, 1968) were interpreted as reflecting a passage from Crackington Formation to Bude Formation. Lithologically, however, they belong in the former.   EAE

BUDE FORMATION

The Bude Formation rocks occurring in this district are closely comparable to those of Boscastle and Holsworthy (McKeown and others, 1973; King, 1967). Although probably up to 50 per cent of the formation consists of sandstones and shales indistinguishable from those of the Crackington Formation (Plate 3), certain characteristic facies occur. The most prominent comprises massive sandstone groups up to 20 m in thickness, with the component beds usually over 1 m thick. The sandstone beds are impersistent and of variable thickness, ranging for example from 1 to 5 m in 200 m laterally. The bases of these sandstones are channelled in places and wedge-bedding is common (Plate 4). Load-casts and flute-casts are plentiful,

and some have very complex shapes; elongate flute-casts and groove-casts are also present. Load-casts also occur within the sandstones, commonly in positions where no continuous bedding plane is evident. The tops of the sandstones are commonly rippled, and local sand volcanoes indicate the rapid dewatering of a fluid mass (Burne, 1970). Vertical dewatering structures are numerous and normal to the bedding.

Although the sandstones are generally described as massive, some internal structure can be discerned in places. This consists chiefly of cross-bedding (Plate 5), locally with foresets 0.20 to 0.40 m long, strong lamination and some convolute lamination. Primary current lineation has also been noted in a number of places. A ubiquitous feature of the sandstones is the presence of mudflakes, and at some

Plate 3 Folds at Warren Gutter

Hard turbiditic sandstones and shales of the Bude Formation immediately underlying the Warren Gutter Shale are disposed in folds trending approximately E–W and slightly overturned towards the south. (A 12458).

Plate 4 Wedge-bedded sandstone of the Bude Formation, Yeol Mouth

Sandstones about 40 m below the Tom's Cove Shale show extensive wedge-bedding. Just left of centre in the picture is an intraformational conglomerate containing clasts of shale and sandstone. (A 12462).

localities mudflake conglomerates occur. Dark red to black ferruginous segregations are also common.

When fresh the sandstones are normally greyish green, but they weather to a buff colour and become somewhat friable. Near the base of the formation, however, they seem to be more strongly cemented and less friable.

Examination of the particle size distribution of some of the more friable sandstones showed the presence of a relatively well-sorted saltation population and a more poorly sorted suspension population. The break between the two usually occurs between $3\,\phi$ and $4\,\phi$, within the very fine sand range where considerable mixing of the two populations is evident. This distribution resembles that in sandstones of the Bideford Formation (Edmonds, Williams and Taylor, 1979), such as the Cornborough Sandstone. Since the Cornborough Sandstone and similar rocks pass eastwards into a sequence

containing massive Bude-type sandstones, it is probable that these last comprise sediments derived almost directly from channel distributaries in the delta top and deposited on the delta slope with little re-working (p.14).

Beds up to 20 m thick of highly disturbed and disrupted masses of slumped debris are common in the Bude Formation (Plate 6). Some have a dark grey shaly matrix enclosing fragments of sandstone, and others have a muddy sandy matrix enveloping debris of sandstone and shale; it is probable that one type passes into another. In some cases the slumped bed consists only of a completely unsorted homogeneous sandy silty mudstone or muddy sandstone, and it is considered likely that this kind of material is the end-product of a slump which has brought about complete disaggregation of lithologies. Burne (1970) suggested that the slumped beds resulted from dewatering of poorly sorted silty muds which

Plate 5 Cross-bedded sandstone of the Bude Formation, Oldwalls, Morwenstow

A fallen block of massive sandstone typical of the Bude Formation shows lamination and cross-bedding picked out by differential weathering. Such sandstone commonly appears structureless when unweathered. The sandstone bed from which this block was derived lenses out within thick black shales. (A 12460).

had been emplaced as dense sediment flows, and that the masses of sandstone caught up within the beds were the remains of foundered sand volcanoes which had formed on top of the muds during dewatering. Some of the sandstone debris occurring within the slumped beds, however, forms large disrupted sheets and rolls showing a preferred orientation. This suggests that the debris was ripped up from the sea floor and transported. When the high-density flow finally came to rest the dewatering process could begin, with the consequent production of some sand volcanoes which foundered to add to the disturbed masses of sandstone already present.

Grey and black mudstones and shales reflect the background sedimentation which was periodically interrupted by sandy incursions. The commonest type of mudstone is grey and silty and occurs as bands usually less than 1 m thick between sandstones. It may be micaceous and commonly contains abundant plant debris. Thicker and darker grey sequences of shale and mudstone occur throughout the succession. They are usually less than 3 m thick, but in the higher parts of the succession may be as thick as 20 m. In many cases these darker shales contain no silt or sand and include ironstone bands up to about 20 mm thick. Some shale sequences of this type contain groups of sandstones up to about 0.15 m thick usually exhibiting well-developed small flute-, prod- and groove-casts and probably representing distal turbidites.

The other main group of mudstones and shales are of more restricted occurrence in the succession but form more continuous marker horizons of great use in correlation. They are

Plate 6   Slumped bed of the Bude Formation north of Sandy Mouth

A massive slumped bed about 80 m above the Sandy Mouth Shale contains inclusions of shale and sandstone. It is overlain by dark grey shales with thin ironstone seams. (A 12456).

black and sulphurous, with bands of calcareous concretions commonly containing goniatites. Spindle-shaped coprolites, probably from fish, occur scattered within many of these shales, and some fish remains have been found, notably in the Tom's Cove Shale and Saturday's Pit Shale. Each bed is characteristically of silty mudstone at its base. Progressively darker grey and less silty material with coprolites usually lies above the silty mudstone, and is succeeded by concretions containing goniatites. More coprolites may be present above the concretions and the bed becomes increasingly silty, less sulphurous, and paler grey towards the top. Thin impersistent sandstones with small tool marks on their bases are also fairly common in these shales and mudstones and may represent distal turbidites. The shales have been used as marker horizons by King (1966, 1967) and Freshney and Taylor (1972).

A facies of grey to dark grey flaggy siltstones and sand-stones showing ripple-drift cross-lamination was described by King (1967) and Freshney, McKeown and Williams (1972). Xiphosurid trails in it were first noted by King (1965), but few have been recorded in the Bude district.

The stratigraphy of the Bude Formation is displayed in a folded succession stretching southwards from Marsland Cliff [170 208] to Bude. The succession youngs southwards from the Hartland Quay Shale to the Warren Gutter Shale, which is repeated twice in the centre of the synclinorium around Duckpool. On the southern side of the synclinorium the formation youngs northwards from Wanson Mouth, south of Bude, to Duckpool. The southern succession has been described in some detail by King (1967) as far north as Northcott Mouth, beyond which faulting renders interpretation difficult. However, elucidation of the stratigraphy in the less faulted northern succession from Marsland Cliff to Duckpool has facilitated the compilation shown in Figure 3.

The succession commences at Marsland Cliff above a shale comparable in its general faunal assemblage to the Hartland Quay Shale which has yielded goniatites of the *Gastrioceras amaliae* horizon (Edmonds, Williams and Taylor, 1979). About 50 m of medium-bedded sandstones with shaly intercalations separate this shale from a higher 2-m shale which has been correlated with the Longpeak Shale of the Bideford district. Between the Longpeak Shale and the Tom's Cove Shale lie thickly to medium-bedded sandstones with some shales and with slumped beds at 550 m[1] and 650 m above the base of the Embury Shale. The Tom's Cove Shale (Lovell, 1965) crops out near Yeolmouth [2013 1622] and is succeeded by approximately 70 m of thickly to medium-bedded sandstones with a few shales and with a slumped bed half-way up the sequence, and these sandstones are overlain by the Saturday's Pit Shale. The Tom's Cove and Saturday's Pit shales have yielded fish remains and coprolites but no goniatites. A variable sequence of sandstones and shales overlies the Saturday's Pit Shale. Many of the shales in this sequence are 7 to 8 m thick and contain thin ironstone bands; slumped beds are common, as at 900 and 935 m above the base of the Embury Shale. The top 55 m of beds are characterised by thickly bedded and massive sandstones with few shales. The overlying Sandy Mouth Shale is about 13 to 14 m thick. Ramsbottom (1970) described the holotype of *Anthracoceratoides cornubiensis* from the Sandy Mouth Shale and suggested that this horizon represented the Margam Marine Band in Westphalian A in South Wales, but structural evidence suggests that the Sandy Mouth Shale occurs higher in the sequence.

The Sandy Mouth Shale is overlain by another variable succession with many groups of thick and massive sandstones, as between 1340 and 1358 m. Shale bands up to 2 or 3 m thick and containing thin ironstones are fairly common to about 1300 m. A number of slumped beds, generally less than 10 m thick, occur in the succession up to about 1250 m; some massive slumped beds up to 25 m thick have been recorded above this, particularly between 1460 and 1520 m. The succession above 1300 m is characterised by shales, mudstones and siltstones in groups commonly over 10 m thick. A 14-m shale band with its base at 1400 m contains many ironstone bands, and is succeeded by a 2-m sandstone overlain by 26 m of shales and siltstones with some sandstone bands. Some of these thin sandstones towards the top of the shale sequence show distinct grading, and sand volcanoes also occur around this level. Many of the thicker argillaceous units between the Sandy Mouth Shale and the Warren Gutter Shale show a pronounced parallel silty banding. The Warren Gutter Shale lies near the top of the Bude Formation of the district and is about 10 m thick; it contains a band of calcareous concretions which yielded fish remains, such as *Rhabdoderma sp.* and various palaeoniscid scales, while a further nodular horizon near the middle of the shale has yielded goniatites of the 'Anthracoceras' aegiranum horizon, which marks the junction between Westphalian B and C. The Warren Gutter Shale is overlain by 30 m of medium-bedded sandstones. It is possible that the argillaceous rocks

around Kilkhampton [254 115] and Tamar Lake [293 112] represent higher Bude Formation strata in the core of the main synclinorium.

The total thickness of Westphalian rocks exposed along the Bude coastline is about 1630 m, of which the Bude Formation amounts to some 1290 m. Firm correlations can be made between the Embury Shale and Gull Rock Shale, 125 m apart in the Crackington Formation in north Cornwall, and the *Gastrioceras subcrenatum* and Cefn Cribbwr marine bands, 120 to 150 m apart in South Wales, although the two sequences are turbidite basinal and Coal Measures respectively. However, higher in the succession this close comparison disappears. If the Hartland Quay Shale equates with the Margam Marine Band (Edmonds, Williams and Taylor, 1979), the 215 m of strata between the Gull Rock Shale and the Hartland Quay Shale in south-west England are equivalent to 50 to 70 m between the Cefn Cribbwr and Margam marine bands in South Wales and to 80 m between the *Gastrioceras listeri* and *Gastrioceras amaliae* marine bands in the Pennines. The correlation of the Warren Gutter Shale with the Cefn Coed, Mansfield and Skipsey's marine bands provides a further comparison of successions, about 1290 m of Bude Formation between the Hartland Quay and Warren Gutter shales being equivalent to about 530 m of Coal Measures in South Wales and to about 700 m in the Pennines. An expanded succession in south-west England is readily accounted for by the introduction of thick sands during deltaic sedimentation (p.14).   E C F

To the north of the Embury anticlinorium only the lowest parts of the Bude Formation are found, in a synclinorium at Brownspear Beach [2240 2340]. At Sandhole Rock [2185 2088] the Hartland Quay Shale occurs at beach level but the faulted and slipped patch of Bude Formation in the cliff above is too small and ill-defined to show on the published map. At Brownspear Beach the typical thick sandstones are rather sparse but the 120 m of Bude Formation exposed show other characteristic features such as channelling and slumped beds. The nodular Longpeak Shale is a prominent marker horizon in the lower part of the formation in the northern part of the district.   R T T

The Bude Formation coastal outcrop between Clovelly [318 248] and Portledge [388 248] is strongly folded and faulted, and greatly obscured by landslip, but the strata young generally southwards, up to a horizon about 150 m above the Longpeak Shale, and the succession appears to resemble that exposed on the western coast. Reddish brown and purple staining affects the sandstones near to the Permian outlier, and this phenomenon was also noted inland. In the inland areas in the north-eastern part of the district, the Bude Formation is represented by a sequence containing many thickly bedded and massive sandstones, with subordinate shales, silty and sandy shales, and siltstones, in which the arenaceous beds greatly predominate. Most of the good exposures are found in the Torridge valley, but the formation is poorly exposed in the main.   B J W

The Bude Formation in the south-east, as elsewhere, is taken as extending down to include the lowest of the massive sandstones found to be typical of these beds. The basal unit is marked by a sandy ridge which is locally displaced by faults but generally runs slightly north of east from Lashbrook [4305 0568] through Highweek [446 057] and the

---

1 The base of the Embury Shale provides a datum for the Upper Carboniferous succession of the cliff sections.

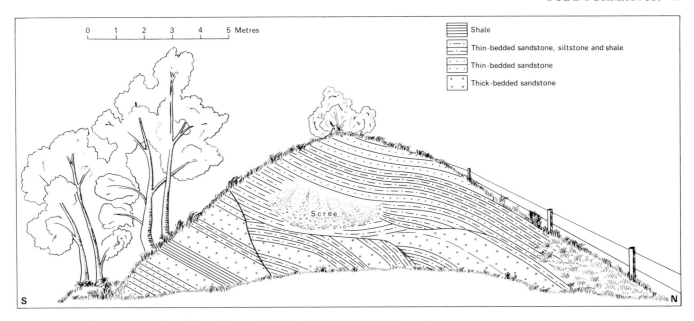

Shale
Thin-bedded sandstone, siltstone and shale
Thin-bedded sandstone
Thick-bedded sandstone

Figure 4   Old quarry north of Thornbury: folded and faulted Bude Formation strata

northern outskirts of Black Torrington to Sheepwash [486 063]. This feature is formed by a group of sandstones with subordinate shales. The sandstones are commonly greenish grey or brown, fine-grained and thickly bedded, but include a good deal of buff sugary sandstone which is locally micaceous.

Northwards from these basal beds, in the area defined by Chilsworthy, Bradworthy, Buckland Filleigh and Sheepwash, the Bude Formation comprises thickly bedded and massive sandstones together with thinner sandstones, shales, silty shales and siltstones. The amount of shale decreases northwards and westwards to give a predominantly arenaceous formation.

The thicker sandstones typically show little internal structure, apart from poorly developed grading. They are fine- or fine- to medium-grained with a good deal of argillaceous material, and are grey or greenish grey when fresh, weathering to brown. Plant fragments are fairly common in both thickly bedded and thinly bedded sandstones. Beds of the former are typically a metre or so thick, of the latter generally less than 0.3 m.

Throughout the south-eastern corner of the district the lithologies of the Bude Formation are reflected in the topography. Ridges predominantly of sandstone, and commonly pock-marked by small disused quarries and pits (Figures 4 and 5), alternate with ENE-trending valleys cut in shales, mudstones, siltstones and thin sandstones.   E A E

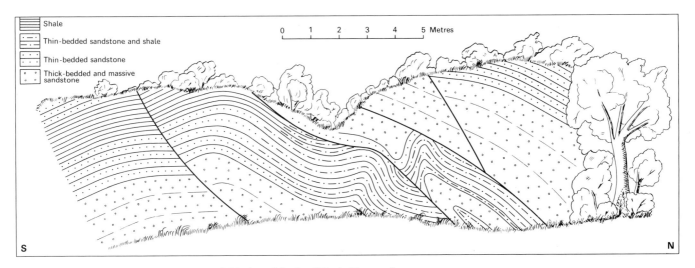

Shale
Thin-bedded sandstone and shale
Thin-bedded sandstone
Thick-bedded and massive sandstone

Figure 5   Quarry at Pitt, Shebbear: folded and faulted Bude Formation strata

CONDITIONS OF DEPOSITION

The area south of the present district shows typical turbiditic lithologies, with distal turbidites of the lower Namurian giving way to proximal turbidites of the more sandstone-rich upper Namurian. In general goniatite faunas are scattered throughout the Namurian succession, but in upper Namurian and Westphalian strata they are restricted to marine bands such as the Embury Shale and Gull Rock Shale. This points to a Namurian sea giving way to brackish-water conditions with sporadic marine incursions. The marine shales dating from these incursions commonly show evidence of fish, perhaps tolerant to low salinity, followed by goniatites which are truly marine, followed by a reversion to less saline waters with fish, and finally a return to brackish-water conditions. The presence of abundant carbonaceous plant material and the trace fossil *Planolites ophthalmoides* supports the view that most of the strata between the marine shales originated in brackish water.

The Crackington Formation was probably deposited largely by turbidity currents in a marine basin forming an east–west arm of the sea. There is strong evidence (Selwood and others, in prep.) for a southern shoreline to this basin in the English Channel. The northern shoreline lay in South Wales, and it is probable that the basin closed to the east. Probably less than 500 m of Crackington Formation sediments accumulated in this basin in fairly shallow water.

Towards the end of the Namurian some restriction of the connection with the main sea area to the west took place, possibly brought about by increased tectonic activity which also caused an influx of sandy detritus into the basin. Deltas extended southwards into north Devon, with subaerial and subaqueous delta-top sediments being deposited in the Bideford district as the Bideford Formation (Edmonds, Williams and Taylor, 1979). Channel-fill sandstones, such as the Cornborough Sandstone, can be traced eastwards towards South Molton, and they pass laterally into sandstones typical of the massive sandstone facies of the Bude Formation (Freshney, Beer and Wright, 1979). The Bude Formation sandstones, although slightly finer in grain-size than those of the Bideford Formation, show a similar grain-size distribution (pp. 9, 16). This suggests that the massive sandstones of the Bude Formation may have been derived from sand spilling from the seaward ends of the delta distributary channels, whose infilling sediments are represented by such sandstones as the Cornborough Sandstone. Many of the sedimentary features of the Bude Formation sandstones are indicative of underflow conditions, and some workers have referred to these rocks as turbidites (Ashwin, 1958; Lovell, 1965). However, such features as cross-bedding, wedge-bedding, primary current lineation, and particle size distribution are suggestive of deposition in fluviatile or deltaic conditions, most likely on the delta slopes with the massive sandstones originating within channels eroded in these slopes. These channels probably led from the distributaries which discharged their sediment loads at the edges of the deltas. The similarity in sorting characteristics between the massive Bude Formation sandstones and the channel sandstones of the Bideford Formation indicates a continuity of sedimentation through from delta top to upper delta slope. The impersistence of sandstones within the Bude Formation suggests that sedimentation was taking place mainly on the upper parts of the delta slopes. An inferred southern hinterland in the English Channel area suggests that the basin was too narrow, perhaps only about 150 km from north to south, for deep water sedimentation.

Thus general indications are of a narrow brackish sea, with deltaic deposits entering from both north and south and with restricted connection with a major sea to the west. Tectonic activity crumpled up the Carboniferous deposits and brought sedimentation to an end. It is suggested that Bude Formation sediments accumulated on a low-angle delta slope and that small changes in sea-level resulted in either shallowing to a few metres or deepening sufficiently to allow marine incursions bringing goniatite faunas. During these incursions the deltas in the northern part of the basin receded, perhaps to about mid-Wales, and euxinic black muds were deposited over much of south-west England. Thin sole-marked sandstones within the black marine shales reflect the action of minor and infrequent turbidity currents. Grey mudstones and shales represent background argillaceous sedimentation during relative quiescence in tectonic activity when little sandy detritus was arriving from the hinterland. It is considered that the slumped beds were produced by sediments tumbling down submarine slopes in response, perhaps, to earth tremors or to the sudden dumping of sediment load from distributaries. Movement of such a mass produced increasing comminution of the unconsolidated material within it, and in some cases a coarsely heterogeneous slump was reduced to a mudflow.

The massive thick sandstones of the Bude Formation probably reflect movement by low-density bottom-currents within shallow channels descending the delta slopes, but it is also possible that some mass sand-flows took place, this being especially true of those sandstones showing complete lack of internal structures. Probably bottom-currents graded into mass flows of waterlogged sands; some sandstones show a lateral passage from laminated through convoluted lamination and bedding to structureless.

The flaggy sandstones and siltstones which locally bear belinurid tracks were probably deposited by gentle currents flowing along the bottom beneath only a few metres of water.

Analysis of current direction indicators shows a main early derivation from the west-south-west, but in late Crackington Formation times and in Bude Formation times up to the deposition of the Sandy Mouth Shale flow was from between north-west and north-east. Figure 6 shows current directions indicated by various sedimentary structures within sequences of strata between the main marker shales. It is probable that directions indicated within the main part of the Crackington Formation represent axial flow along the depositional trough, and that subsequent southerly encroachment by deltas introduced currents and sediments from a northerly direction. The few channels in the Bude Formation whose trend it was possible to measure show a north–south orientation. The strong relatively unipolar source indicated for the sequence of strata above the Sandy Mouth Shale may reflect the presence of a large southerly-extending lobe of a delta to the east of the present coastline north of Bude. Another possibility is that the sediment was being derived from a north–south shoreline developing to the east.   ECF

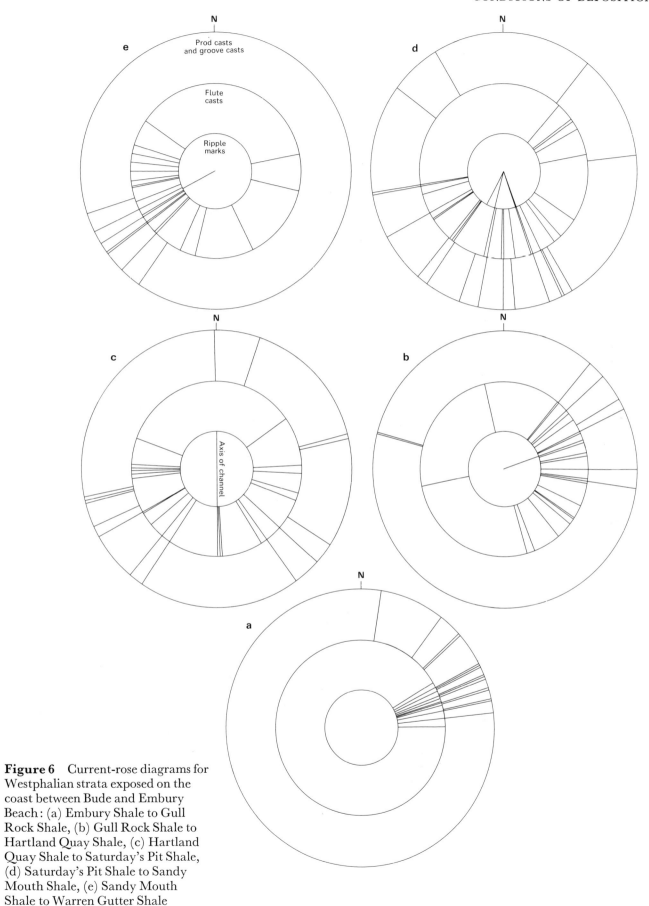

Figure 6 Current-rose diagrams for Westphalian strata exposed on the coast between Bude and Embury Beach: (a) Embury Shale to Gull Rock Shale, (b) Gull Rock Shale to Hartland Quay Shale, (c) Hartland Quay Shale to Saturday's Pit Shale, (d) Saturday's Pit Shale to Sandy Mouth Shale, (e) Sandy Mouth Shale to Warren Gutter Shale

MINERALOGY AND PETROGRAPHY

Shales

X-ray diffraction techniques were used to examine 39 samples from the Embury Shale, Tom's Cove Shale, Sandy Mouth Shale and Warren Gutter Shale, including contained nodules and ironstones (charts DX 1554–1592). The results show that the clay mineral suite consists dominantly of illite; subordinate chlorite and kaolinite are present in amounts which appear to reflect the degree of deformation (and consequent recrystallisation) of the shale. Shales from relatively undeformed outcrops at Embury Beach [2135 1955] and Sandy Mouth [2015 1009] contain illite plus kaolinite, whereas samples from the intensely crumpled outcrop of the Warren Gutter Shale at [2010 1106] contain illite plus chlorite. The Tom's Cove Shale at [2010 0772] is vertical but undeformed and contains both chlorite and kaolinite, though rarely in the same sample. The absence of pyrite from the Warren Gutter Shale at [2010 1106] suggests that this mineral may be involved in the formation of chlorite from the breakdown of kaolinite.

Amounts of quartz, and also kaolinite where present, generally increase upwards. This may reflect silting-up of the basin and perhaps increasingly brackish waters. The Tom's Cove Shale at [2010 0772] lies 0.5 m below a non-marine grey shale which contains significantly more kaolinite, suggesting a link between kaolinite content and brackish waters.

The calcareous nodules within the shales are mainly composed of ankerite. One such nodule from the Sandy Mouth Shale [2015 1009] is cut by a thin vein containing dickite and sphalerite. Ironstone ribs in the shales are invariably composed of siderite and this mineral is also abundant in some non-fissile, blocky mudstones. A yellowish white efflorescence on the black 'sulphurous shales' is a mineral of the jarosite-natrojarosite group. Its absence from the pyrite-free Warren Gutter Shale suggests that it is formed by oxidation of pyrite coupled with leaching of potassium from illite.

Sandstones

Petrographical studies were made of 16 sandstone beds occurring in the coastal exposures of the Bude Formation. Half were typical Bude Formation sandstones (pp. 8–9), massive and thickly bedded and friable and buff-coloured when weathered, and the other half were thinly bedded, hard and dark grey, resembling the characteristic sandstones of the Crackington Formation (p. 4). The samples were collected in pairs, specimens of each lithology being obtained as near to one another as possible at eight localities (E 47288, 47291–5, 47302–3, 47306–10, 47312–4).

In thin section both sandstone types consist essentially of a framework of quartz grains with minor feldspar, mica and lithic fragments, held in a matrix of recrystallised silt and clay-grade material. The maximum grain size of the framework components (Table 1) is on average greater for the more massive sandstones, but the thinly bedded sandstones show a greater range of size, from silt (E 47288, 47295) to medium sand. Many of the quartz grains show strain extinction and a few in each thin section exhibit Boehm strain lamellae; they are of high sphericity and subangular to subrounded. Optically continuous outgrowths from the quartz grains are fairly common and in some massive sandstones this has produced a patchy development of interlocking silica. However, in most specimens the outgrowths are usually no more than a narrow border between the quartz grains and the matrix.

Lithic fragments include acid and basic volcanic rocks, schist, schistose quartzite, quartzite, phyllite, siltstone, argillite and chert and are slightly more abundant in the massive sandstones. Feldspar grains are generally fresh and are mostly sodic plagioclase with rare perthitic K-feldspar. Flakes of detrital muscovite and chloritised mica are generally more common in the thinly bedded sandstones. Both sandstone types contain the accessory minerals tourmaline, zircon and sphene, but three massive sandstones contain epidote in addition (E 47291–2, 47310). All of the specimens contain minor amounts of granular carbonate which X-ray diffraction checks show to be a mixture of siderite and ankerite. It forms a patchy cement of secondary

Table 1 Average modes (volume per cent) for arenaceous rocks from the Bude Formation.

	1		2	
	Range	Mean	Range	Mean
Quartz	44.2–59.3	53.7	40.8–61.8	51.7
Feldspar	1.7–4.0	2.9	1.1–4.5	2.5
Lithic fragments	7.2–13.6	9.2	5.2–13.0	7.6
Detrital mica	1.3–4.8	2.7	0.4–9.1	3.6
Matrix+ silica cement	20.0–33.4	25.6	28.6–35.0	31.4
Accessories +opaques	0.7–2.2	1.4	0.7–2.3	1.2
Carbonate	0.2–10.2	4.5	0.2–4.3	2.0
Maximum grain size	0.15–0.37 mm	0.26 mm	0.05–0.36 mm	0.18 mm

1   Massive and thickly bedded sandstones (8 specimens)

2   Thinly bedded sandstones (8 specimens)

origin and is most abundant in the more weathered specimens of massive sandstone.

The main difference between the two sandstone lithologies relates to the amount of matrix present and the degree of recrystallisation it has experienced. Although both types of sandstone can be classified as greywackes, modal analyses (Table 1) show that the thinly bedded sandstones contain significantly more matrix material than do the massive sandstones. Further examination by X-ray diffractometry reveals that the former contain appreciable amounts of chlorite but little or no kaolinite, whereas kaolinite is present in all but one of the massive sandstones examined (E 47308) and is commonly more abundant than chlorite in these specimens (charts DX 1752, 1758–60, 1774–79). These results suggest that the greater resistance to weathering shown by the thinly bedded sandstones is due mainly to extensive recrystallisation of original clay minerals in the matrix to form a more cohesive intergrowth of chlorite, sericite and probably submicrocrystalline silica. The greater abundance of kaolinite relative to chlorite in most of the massive sandstones indicates that clay minerals in the matrices have not undergone the same degree of recrystallisation; this would account for the friable nature of some of these sandstones when weathered.

It seems reasonable to suppose that during regional folding the thinner bedded sandstones with a greater amount of matrix would be more susceptible to recrystallisation than would the massive sandstone typical of the Bude Formation.

RJM

DETAILS

CRACKINGTON FORMATION

Coastal details are given southwards and northwards from the Embury anticlinorium, where the oldest rocks of the district are exposed.

Coastal section

Embury Beach to Knaps Longpeak

In the core of the Embury anticlinorium [2159 1954] 12 m of turbiditic sandstones with groove-casts and linear sole marks are interbedded with shales and siltstones.

The Embury Shale is exposed at the southern side of Broad Bench Cove [2150 1958] and comprises 3.5 m of grey sulphurous shale; carbonate concretions 0.5 m above the base yielded *Gastrioceras subcrenatum*.

The following section between northings [1956] and [1904][1] shows:

	Thickness m
Base of Gull Rock Shale	
Sandstones containing mud-flake conglomerate	1.0
Sandstones	1.5
Black shales and sandstones	1.0
Muddy sandstones with bands of graded sandstone	7.0
Slumped bed	6.5
Shales	2.6
Sharply bedded sandstones and shales	5.5
Shales with thin sandstones showing groove-casts, tool marks and flute-casts. Some thicker sandstones towards the top. Bottom 2 m very shaly and probably equivalent to the Wanson Beds of Mackintosh (1965)	49.2
Thin sharply bedded turbiditic sandstones with shales	36.0
Sandstones with slurried beds, and with reworked nodules containing goniatites	11.0
Top of the Embury Shale	

The Gull Rock Shale is exposed north-east of Knaps Longpeak at the base of the cliff at northing [1903]. Some 6 m of black to dark grey shales contain two layers of calcareous concretions, 4.2 and 4.74 m from the base, which have yielded *Gastrioceras circumnodosum*, *G. coronatum* and *G. listeri*, all characteristic of the *G. listeri* Marine Band. Below the nodules framboidal pyrite occurs; above the nodules the shales are sulphurous.

Knaps Longpeak to Welcombe Mouth

The cliff section shows strata between the Gull Rock Shale and the Hartland Quay Shale. There is much repetition by folding, and NW–SE wrench faults are common between Welcombe Mouth [212 180] and Marsland Mouth [211 175]. The Hartland Quay Shale may crop out in the top of the cliff at [2125 1825]. All the strata belong to the Crackington Formation, but a few massive sandstones of Bude Formation type are present, as at [2111 1822].

The following section extends from an anticline at northing [1864] to a syncline at northing [1859]:

1 Where northings alone are used, the eastings are the intersection with the cliff base along the western coast.

	Thickness m
Well-bedded sandstones with intervening shales, siltstones and mudstones	43.0
Shales with thin stringy sandstone bands	3.5
Thinly bedded sandstones	2.0
Sharply defined well-bedded sandstones with intervening shales and siltstones	7.2
Sandstone	3.0
Sharply defined well-bedded sandstones with shales and siltstones	3.0
Shales with thin sandstone bands	3.0
Dark grey shales and mudstones with thin sandstones generally less than 20 mm thick but locally up to 0.20 m	5.4
Shales	1.0

The following section extends from an anticline at northing [1829] to a syncline at northing [1826]:

	Thickness m
Massive sandstones	4.6
Sharply defined well-bedded sandstones	7.7
Sandstone	1.5
Thinly bedded sandstones	2.1
Slumped bed	2.0
Fissile thin brown sandstones with mudstones	9.3
Sandstone	2.7
Well-bedded sandstones with thin sandstones in the middle of the section	5.4
Sandstone	2.8
Shales and mudstones with thin laminated sandstones	3.6
Sandstone	1.0

The succession in a syncline at northing [1814] and an anticline at northing [1804] is:

	Thickness m
Mainly thick-bedded sandstones	10.5
Greyish green massive sandstone with large load-casts	5.6
Thinly bedded turbiditic sandstones with many mudstone bands	19.0
Bands of silty shale up to 1 m thick with thin sandstones	3.1
Sandstone	1.0
Medium-bedded sandstones	8.0

The topmost beds of the Crackington Formation crop out south-west of Marsland Mouth between a syncline at northing [1708] and an anticline at northing [1700]:

	Thickness m
Sharply defined sandstones up to 1 m thick with many mudstone and siltstone beds. Sandstones become thicker in depth with fewer shale bands	75.0
Shales, rather disturbed, with ironstone bands	1.8
Sharply defined sandstones up to 1 m thick with much slaty siltstone	17.0
Silty mudstone with some sandstone bands showing large load-casts	7.0
Sandstone	2.0
Hard greyish green sandstones with much interbedded shale and siltstone. Flute-casts, rill marks and groove-casts common	12.0

Litter Mouth

The Hartland Quay Shale is exposed at Litter Mouth [2067 1697] as follows:

	Thickness m
Silty dark grey shale yielding *Caneyella* and anthracoceratids; layer of calcareous nodules about 2 m from the top	2.58
Sandstone	0.25
Dark grey shales with a band of calcareous nodules 0.45 m from the base; shale yielded unidentifiable goniatites and conodonts, ostracods and fish fragments; coprolites, probably from fish, are common	1.23

E C F

Gull Rock Beach to Elmscott Beach

On Gull Rock Beach [2144 2001] the Gull Rock Shale, which crops out in the northern limb of the Embury anticlinorium and has yielded *Gastrioceras listeri*, *G. circumnodosum*, *Homoceratoides* aff. *divaricatus*, *Dunbarella sp.*, *Rhabdoderma sp.*, and plant remains including *Annularia*, shows the following section:

	Thickness m
Laminated siltstones with siderite nodules and small calcareous nodules	0.71
Laminated silty shales with small goniatite-bearing nodules	0.30
Laminated silty shales with large calcareous nodules, up to 250 mm across and 150 mm thick, containing abundant goniatites	0.76
Soft nodular shales, poorly exposed	0.91
Black laminated shales with pyrite along bedding, in tubular forms cutting across bedding, and in small framboidal aggregates	1.60
Black laminated shales with sideritic layers and a thin sandstone at the top	1.68

At this locality the shale succession appears to be complete, without any evidence of the penecontemporaneous erosion noted in the Hartland area to the north (Edmonds, Williams and Taylor, 1979). The pyritous zone within the shale is a widespread feature of the horizon.

The succession youngs northwards into a broad synclinorial area between Osland Beach [2180 2080] and Elmscott Beach [2210 2145]. This area is much faulted and landslipped but a number of exposures of the Hartland Quay Shale occur at beach level in a series of folds to the north and south of Sandhole Rock [2185 2088]. The succession through the Hartland Quay Shale commencing north of Sandhole Rock at [2192 2098] is as follows:

	Thickness m
Thinly bedded, flaggy siltstones	2.00
Thinly bedded sandstones with silty interbeds	0.40
Very thinly bedded sandstones with flaggy siltstones	3.00
Thinly bedded sandstones	0.60
Slumped bed	0.30
Thinly bedded sandstones	0.50
Hartland Quay Shale. Black laminated shales with 10-mm silty bands. Fusiform phosphatic coprolite pellets are concentrated in the top 0.3 m. Horizons of calcareous nodules, some of them fossiliferous, occur 1.2 and 1.8 m from the top	2.20
Thin and medium-bedded sandstones	1.70
Thinly bedded sandstones with partings of black siltstone and shale	1.45
Black shales with silty laminae, and a band of calcareous nodules 0.2 m from the top	0.55
Flaggy and silty mudstones with some very thin sandy bands	2.00
Thinly bedded sandstones	0.50
Laminated, flaggy sandstones and siltstones	0.55
Laminated sandstone	1.10

Thickness
m

Composite sandstone formed of units showing thin ripple-drift
cross-bedding — 4.50

Thinly bedded sandstones and laminated mudstones — 1.00

Laminated silty sandstones and sandstones showing ripple-
drift cross-bedding — 1.50

The Hartland Quay Shale has yielded *Gastrioceras* cf. *amaliae*
[2192 2094], *Caneyella*, small turreted gastropods, *Anthracoceratites
sp.*, *?G. amaliae* and mollusc spat [2194 2093], and *Anthracoceratites sp.* [2175 2081]. The base of the sandstone overlying the
thin nodular shale 3.15 m below the Hartland Quay Shale
[2184 2077] has yielded poorly preserved *G.* cf. *amaliae*.

The top Crackington Formation strata of this locality contain a
few sandstones of Bude Formation type; particularly massive
sandstones are visible high in the cliff [2175 2050] south of Osland
Beach.

An exposure [2209 2105], possibly slipped, contains the
following section:

Thickness
m

Thinly and medium-bedded sandstones with silty partings — 2.00

Shales with silty bands, passing downwards into siltstones — 1.13

Thin sandstone with large load-casts on base and containing
fusiform pellets — 0.10 to 0.20

Shales with silty bands and some fusiform coprolite pellets
at the top, and scattered nodules — 1.88

Sandstone — 0.43

Thin sandstones with silty partings and a few sideritic
nodules — 2.36

Shales with silty laminae and a horizon of silty calcareous
nodules — 1.00

Shales — 1.82

Thin sandstones — seen

No fossil material apart from phosphatic fusiform coprolite pellets
has been obtained from this locality. A similar occurrence of shales
with coprolite pellets and scattered decalcified nodules containing
mollusc spat occurs near the cliff top at [2186 2054]. The shales at
these two localities bear a superficial resemblance to the Hartland
Quay Shale, but their positions in the cliff make this correlation
unlikely. It is suggested that they are the Longpeak Shale which, at
Litter Mouth to the south, is similarly divided into two by sandstones. At Sandhole Cliff [2213 2090] a 1.3-m shale containing
coprolite pellets occurs within a sequence of thinly and medium-
bedded sandstones; it probably corresponds to shales about 40 m
above the Longpeak Shale in sections farther north (p. 28).

Elmscott Beach to Hole Rock

To the north of the wrench faults on Elmscott Beach successively
older beds come on across an anticlinorial structure, and an anticline at Cow Rock [2227 2162] (Plate 9) contains the Gull Rock
Shale which has yielded *Gastrioceras circumnodosum*, *G. listeri*,
Anthracoceratites, and carbonised wood preserved in calcareous
nodules. The overlying sandstone has goniatites caught up in the
base. A slumped bed is revealed below the Gull Rock Shale in the
core of the anticline on the foreshore. It corresponds to a similar
bed below the Gull Rock Shale on Gull Rock Beach over 1.5 km to
the south, and it seems likely that this slumped horizon originally
extended at least 3 km N–S. To the north the Gull Rock Shale is
exposed in anticlines on the foreshore to the south [2210 2191] and
north [2220 2207] of Mansley Rock.

In the following section, between Mansley Beach and Hole Rock
[2215 2262], the base of the Bude Formation is the base of the
sandstone overlying the Hartland Quay Shale. The beds are
disposed in several folds.

Thickness
m

Disturbed and contorted shales with sandstone clasts and
broken plates of siderite; some fusiform pellets — 0.20

Hartland Quay Shale

Laminated black shales with sideritic bands and fusiform
coprolite pellets, separated by a thin sandstone below
from silty laminated shales with scattered decalcified
nodules at the top, some containing goniatites — 1.68

Thinly bedded and some medium-bedded sandstones
interbedded with siltstones in about equal proportions.
Some thin sandstones are cross-bedded. Casts and
impressions of goniatites on the base of the lowest
sandstone — 4.67

Black shales, silty and with slightly calcareous concretions
in bottom 150 mm, underlain by siltstones and shales
with thin sandstone bands — 0.94

Medium-bedded sandstones — 3.38

Flaggy, laminated, graded siltstones with a few thin
sandstones — 1.60

Thinly and medium-bedded sandstones; some interbedded
siltstones — 6.17

Two thick composite sandstone beds — 2.46

Thin sandstones with silty partings — 1.22

Dark grey to black laminated shales with thin sandstone
and siltstone bands 3–50 mm thick — 1.17

Thin sandstones interbedded with siltstones — 4.88

Thinly and medium-bedded sandstones interbedded with
laminated and graded siltstones — 6.17

Composite sandstone bed — 1.12

Thinly bedded sandstones underlain by medium-bedded
sandstone — 4.93

Laminated siltstones with some thin sandstones — 2.05

Thin silty sandstone with laminated top underlain by two
thicker sandstones — 4.29

Graded siltstones with sandy laminae and a few thin
sandstones — 4.83

Composite sandstone bed — 1.27

Laminated siltstones, some graded and some with ripple-
drift cross-bedding, and a few thin sandstones — 7.31

Thin sandstones — 1.42

Laminated siltstones with some thinly and medium-bedded
sandstones. Some grading and ripple-drift cross-bedding in
siltstones and thinner sandstones. Ratio of siltstone to
sandstone about 7:3 — 12.04

Thinly bedded sandstones with silty partings and some
graded siltstones or silty sandstones — 10.01

Two sandstone beds — 1.27

Siltstones showing some grading and convolution, with thin
sandstones showing ripple-drift cross-bedding — 4.42

Thinly and some medium-bedded sandstones with interbedded siltstones. Medium sandstones usually cross-bedded
at top — 16.94

Dark grey to black silty shales with some thin sandstones — 1.22

Composite sandstone bed — 0.69

Dark grey silty shales underlain by dark grey siltstones with
thin sandstones — 4.65

Composite sandstone bed — 1.83

Laminated and graded siltstones with one composite
sandstone. Some graded siltstone or silty sandstone beds
up to 0.2 m thick — 7.57

Thin sandstones interbedded with siltstones — 11.56

Composite sandstone bed — 1.47

Thinly and medium-bedded sandstones, some laminated or
composite — 4.93

[*Possible small fault*]

Thinly bedded sandstones with some silty partings — 5.74

	Thickness
	m
Dark grey laminated siltstones with a few very thin sandstones	2.29
Thin sandstones, some interbedded with siltstones	10.85
Dark grey shales with silty laminae	0.69
Thinly and some medium-bedded sandstones interbedded with siltstones	13.00
Sandstone	1.07
Thin sandstones, some interbedded with siltstones	5.38
Sandstone	1.19
Thin sandstones and shales	0.61
Gull Rock Shale. Black shales with calcareous nodules containing goniatites	seen

Nodules from the Hartland Quay Shale south of Hole Rock [2215 2262] have yielded *Anthracoceratites sp.*, closely comparable with those from the Hartland Quay Shale at Windbury Point north of the district [2877 2676] (Edmonds, Williams and Taylor, 1979), juvenile goniatites and spat. Another exposure near the cliff top [2229 2261] yielded the following fauna from about 0.3 m above the base of the shale: anthracoceratids, *Gastrioceras* cf. *amaliae* and conodont aggregates including *Hindeodella sp*. The shale horizon 4.67 m below the Hartland Quay Shale in the section at [2218 2262] yielded *Gastrioceras* cf. *amaliae*, indicating a correlation with the fossiliferous nodular shale beneath the Hartland Quay Shale at Hole Rock.   RTT

Inland exposures

Welcombe to Stroxworthy

Exposures in a stream to the north of Welcombe Village, between [2227 1891] and [2294 1896], consist mostly of sandstones with subordinate shales. A shale bed about 6 m thick and containing thin sandstones crops out in a stream at [2236 1892]. Farther upstream occurs an extremely muddy sandstone [2274 1896] which may correlate with the slumped bed that occurs in Embury Cliff about 10 m below the Gull Rock Shale; siltstones containing plant fragments and indeterminate goniatites crop out at [2348 1902]. A stream section between [2423 1889] and [2492 1857] shows interbedded shales and sandstones, the latter up to 0.3 m thick; these rocks resemble the shales and thin sandstones between the Embury Shale and the Gull Rock Shale, the Wanson Beds of Mackintosh (1965). Similar rocks crop out in another stream between [2387 1786] and [2356 1757]. The Gull Rock Shale, black sulphurous shales with laminated concretions yielding *Gastrioceras listeri*, is exposed in a stream at [2491 1735]. Another stream section between [2518 1650] and [2529 1768] shows shales and thin sandstones characteristic of the sequence between the Embury Shale and the Gull Rock Shale. A quarry [2874 1829] north-east of Meddon exposes banded siltstones with some shales and a 1.6-m sandstone. A flooded quarry [3287 1941] shows hard sandstones, some of them flaggy, with mudstones and shales. A small pit [3454 1940] on the banks of the Dipple Water exposes 0.2 m of bedded sandstones and shales.   ECF

South Hole to Firebeacon

A stream section [2234 2000 to 2275 2027] shows sporadic thin sandstones dipping 45°–51°S; vertical thin sandstones and shales strike at 087° at [2275 2023]. At Goldenpark [2321 2015] thinly and medium-bedded sandstones dip 59°/354°[1]. Stream exposures

1 Where dips are given in this form the first number is the angle of dip and the second is its full-circle bearing measured clockwise from True North.

around [2399 2005] are of thinly bedded sandstones and siltstones dipping 58°/350°.

Elmscott to Tosberry Moor

A small quarry [2334 2187] reveals 4.5 m of sandstones 0.25 to 0.3 m thick, with silty partings and some thicker silty beds, dipping 21°/181°. A stream section [2336 2133 to 2388 2256] shows thinly and medium-bedded sandstones in an anticline [2355 2213] whose limbs dip 24°/167° and 80°/002° and which plunges 6°/090°. Load casts on the bases of thin sandstones associated with siltstones [2376 2237] indicate that the beds are overturned dipping 32°/167°. Small anticlines and synclines in thinly bedded sandstones are exposed at the confluence of the stream [2388 2256]; the limbs of the anticline dip 46°/347° and 84°/349° and plunge is 2°/070°. Another stream [2375 2200 to 2369 2221] cuts through thin sandstones with siltstones dipping 17°–58° S. The south face of a quarry at Warriors Lodge [2391 2256] shows thin-bedded sandstones and siltstones folded into a syncline and anticline which are probably continuations of folds visible in the stream to the west.

A stream section [2383 2260 to 2473 2151] shows, at its north-west end, thin sandstones folded into a series of small anticlines and synclines. A considerable thickness of laminated and cleaved siltstones is exposed in the hinge of an anticline 25 m upstream from there. Other exposures along this stream include: thin sandstones with siltstones folded into an anticline [2413 2222] with limbs dipping 82°/360° and 25°/187°; about 6 m of laminated siltstones with some thin sandstones dipping 81°/192° and overturned [2416 2217]; thinly and medium-bedded sandstones overturned and dipping 70°/187° in the northern limb of an anticline [2428 2197] whose southern limb dips 27°/192°; similar rocks in another anticline [2427 2197] plunging 6°/088°; a 3-m slumped bed, of silty shales containing contorted sandstone clasts and with a lens of reddened sandstone at the top, overlain by thin sandstones dipping south [2435 2171]; a strike section in shales, with thin sandstones above and below [2448 2155 to 2462 2153]; black shales with calcareous nodules [2456 2156]. This last exposure shows about 3 m of shales overlain by thin sandstones and siltstones dipping 62°/022°. Nodules occur in two bands 0.30 and 1.52 m below the top of the shales. Some of the nodules have formed round plant fragments. Others contain fusiform coprolite pellets and one yielded fish remains. The composite sequence here, of 2.4 m of shales overlain by about 2 m of thin sandstones capped by 3 m of shales with nodules, bears a relationship to the Gull Rock Shale in a stream to the south (see below) which suggests a correlation with the Hartland Quay Shale. Poor exposures of the shales occur farther upstream [2464 2152; 2473 2151].

A stream east of Docton [2458 2076 to 2462 2153] cuts through: thin sandstones, some interbedded with siltstones, predominantly dipping 25°–45° S [2458 2076 to 2054 2107]; thinly and medium-bedded sandstones folded into an anticline whose limbs dip 38°/202° and 32°/336° [2454 2109]; 3.05 m of vertical siltstones younging north and striking 110° [2457 2121]; Gull Rock Shale [2462 2139]. This last exposure comprises 7.3 m of black shales overlain by very thin silty sandstones, vertical, striking 110° and younging north. A band of nodules, containing poorly preserved goniatites and fusiform coprolite pellets, occurs about 1 m below the top of the shales and has yielded anthracoceratids and *Gastrioceras* cf. *circumnodosum*. Farther downstream vertical sandstones young north. The distance between these fossiliferous shales and the ones described above is about 150 m, measured across the strike of steep or vertical strata, an interval which accords with that between the Gull Rock Shale and the Hartland Quay Shale on the coast.

A stream section [2473 2151 to 2523 2139] shows: thinly and medium-bedded sandstones interbedded with siltstones dipping 51°/012° [2496 2154]; similar sandstones in a syncline whose limbs dip 25°/188° and 68°/004° [2502 2153]; similar sandstones cropping out for 90 m upstream from there and containing two bands of siltstone 1.22 and 3.04 m thick; thin sandstones and siltstones in an anticline [2523 2139] whose limbs dip 75°/017° and 25°/190° and which plunges 3°/107°. An old quarry [2518 2138] exposes sandstones 150 to 300 mm thick with silty partings 3.05 m, overlain by siltstone 0.61 m, sandstones 150 to 300 mm thick with silty partings 1.83 m, sandstones and siltstones 75 to 200 mm thick 0.91 m, and Head 0.60 to 0.90 m; the beds dip 8°/192°.

A stream section [2529 2075 to 2523 2139] shows the following exposures: shales with thin sandstones disposed in small-scale folds [2529 2075]; similar strata in a minor anticline [2519 2084] whose limbs dip 38°/182° and 36°/356°; thin sandstones, siltstones and shales in small open folds [2514 2097]. Shales and contorted shales with thin sandstones crop out 150 m downstream, and shales are also exposed in a ditch [2534 2105] west of the stream. A slumped bed [2515 2120] consists of a mass of sandstone in a structureless dark grey silty matrix.

A stream section [2523 2139 to 2627 2104] exposes thin sandstones showing ripple-drift cross-bedding and disposed in a syncline [2528 2134] with limbs dipping 20°/180° and 45°/010°. Between [2568 2122] and [2511 2120] the stream runs along the strike of shales about 1.52 m thick. A band of decalcified nodules in the stream bed about 0.3 m below the top of the shales has yielded *Anthracoceratites sp.*, *Gastrioceras circumnodosum* and *G. listeri*. Other exposures in the stream course include: vertical thinly and medium-bedded sandstones striking 109° and younging north [2606 2102]; grey silty shales [2615 2106], and about 3 m upstream thin sandstones overlain by 3 m of shales dipping 15°/172°; shales and thin sandstones in the north bank [2624 2105] and some 3 m of shales in the south bank; for about 50 m downstream from this last locality, fragments of decalcified nodules with *Gastrioceras listeri* and *Dunbarella sp.*; at about 25 m upstream from the locality, shales containing unfossiliferous decalcified nodules penetrated by tubular structures normal to bedding which may be worm burrows. The fossils were not found *in situ* but come from the Gull Rock Shale; the unfossiliferous nodules may be from the same shale beneath the goniatite-bearing horizon.

Lymebridge to Baxworthy

Milford Water [2344 2276 to 2467 2247] exposes: dark grey siltstones with some thin sandstones in the hinge of a syncline [2345 2275] whose limbs dip 70°/169° and 55°/347°; siltstones and sandstones [2350 2274] in the hinge of an anticline which is offset by a small WNW–ESE dextral wrench fault; similar rocks in a syncline [2353 2275; 2359 2277] which plunges 5° E; thinly bedded sandstones with shale and siltstone partings in fold hinges [2372 2270; 2380 2265; 2393 2258], upstream of the roadbridge at Lymebridge; black shales and siltstones [2405 2254]. A tributary stream [2470 2254] shows thin sandstones and shales dipping 56°/177° and 82°/354° on the flanks of an anticline. An old quarry [2480 2243] exposes 2.59 m of laminated grey siltstones and laminated silty sandstones, showing ripple-drift cross-bedding and dipping 25°/192°.

A stream course from [2467 2247] to [2565 2224] contains isolated exposures of thinly and medium-bedded sandstones usually interbedded with siltstones. The beds dip 66°/360° at [2480 2239], but farther east dips are to the south. In a nearby quarry [2535 2230] thin sandstones interbedded with dark grey siltstones dip 37°/170°. Downstream from [2587 2242] thinly and medium-bedded sandstones dip 76°/010°, and thin sandstones showing ripple-drift cross-bedding dip 30°/185° [2275 2233].

Another stream [2565 2224 to 2648 2193] cuts through thin sandstones interbedded with siltstones. Dips are mainly 20°–36° southerly, but overturned beds dip 70°/187° at [2567 2223] and 58°/182° at [2584 2216]. A stream course from [2659 to 2161] to [2648 2193] shows thin sandstones dipping 62°/007° [2659 2161].

Some 20 m downstream dark grey shales contain small decalcified nodules with goniatite spat. A further 70 m downstream N-dipping thin sandstones crop out and at [2654 2177] black shales yielded a decalcified nodule. These shales may be the Hartland Quay Shale or the Longpeak Shale; the Gull Rock Shale crops out about 550 m to the S.

A stream course [2648 2193 to 2764 2214] contains the following exposures: thin flaggy siltstones and sandstones dipping 35°/187° [2668 2166]; thin sandstones and shales underlain by shales dipping 36°/167° [2693 2202]; upstream to [2752 2206] thin and flaggy sandstones dipping at less than 30° S or horizontal; thin sandstones dipping 35°/037° [2753 2207] and 80°/022° [2764 2214]; thin sandstones cut by a minor strike fault [2757 2210].

A trackway south of Welsford traverses poorly exposed sandstones [2727 2179], but farther south it cuts across 6.1 m of siltstones dipping 15°/207° [2731 2168].

Binworthy Moor to Clifford

Seckington Water [2855 2142 to 2875 2078] contains exposures of thin sandstones dipping 45°/360° [2858 2106] and 60°/002° [2875 2078]. A drainage ditch [2896 2088] east of the stream reveals a 5-m section of disturbed black shales. At Stitworthy [2984 2196] thin sandstones and flaggy silty sandstones dip 15°/158°. An old trackway [3043 2192] traverses dark grey to black laminated shales with a band of sandstone dipping 33°/197°, and shale fragments have been ploughed up in fields to the east and west.

Clifford Water [3050 2116 to 3027 2050] contains sandstones dipping 30°/183°. Shales and siltstones in the stream bed are steep or vertical [3035 2086], at 30 m downstream shales dip south, and at [3030 2052] shales and thin sandstones dip 28°/167°. An old quarry [3042 2110] shows 6.1 m of sandstones 150 to 300 mm thick with interbedded thin siltstones; the dip is 30°/187°. The stream course from [3208 2112] to [3235 2081] exposes thin sandstones dipping 23°/157° [3208 2112], and gently dipping siltstones and shales some 200 m downstream; farther downstream thin sandstones dip 24°/197° [3230 2087]. R T T

Black Torrington to Sheepwash

Shales and silty shales with scattered thin sandstone bands crop out in roadsides and streams in and near Black Torrington. They are locally vertical, strike 100° [4625 0565] or dip 85°/010° [4632 0565] or 55°/355° [4687 0572] to pass below more gently inclined Bude Formation sandstones. Similar strata at the top of the formation in a small north-flowing stream to the east [4771 0564 to 4748 0597] appear to be disposed in folds whose limbs dip about 20°/320°–340° or are vertical trending between 100° and 110°. E A E

BUDE FORMATION

Coastal section

Marsland Cliff to Lower Sharpnose Point

Strata between the Hartland Quay Shale and the Longpeak Shale between northings [1693] and [1691] consist mainly of sandstones, some showing prominent flute-casts on their bases. A slumped mudstone 1.5 m thick occurs 19 m above the base of the section.

The Longpeak Shale crops out at the base of the cliff at northing [1691] as follows:

	Thickness m
Black shales with thin ironstone bands and coprolitic nodules	1.9
Siltstones and sandstones	2.9
Grey siltstones with nodules yielding *Caneyella, Posidonia* [juv.] and goniatite spat	1.0

Strata between the Longpeak Shale and the Tom's Cove Shale are exposed southwards to northing [1644], with the Tom's Cove Shale in the core of a syncline at the top of the cliff:

	Thickness m
Base of Tom's Cove Shale	
Mainly sandstones with a slumped bed (see below)	40.0
Massive greenish grey sandstones with large load-casts	26.0
Dark grey shales	2.8
Sandstones with laminated siltstones and shales	18.0
Sandstones up to 1.5 m thick with load-casts	10.0
Sandstone with slumped bed	1.0
Greyish green sandstones showing wedge-bedding, with some shales	15.0
Slumped bed	1.0
Laminated siltstones and sandstones showing ripple-drift lamination	1.0
Black shales	1.0
Well-bedded sandstones	6.5
Black shaly slumped bed with ironstone bands 2 m from base; some black shales with thin sandstones	8.0
Sandstones with 1-m dark grey silty shale mid-way	8.0
Thin-bedded sandstones and mudstones	6.0
Silty shales and siltstones with sandstones up to 1 m thick and a 1.2-m black shale in middle of sequence	12.0
Massive sandstone with large load-casts	3.0
Black shales	2.0
Sharply bedded sandstones up to 0.8 m thick, with many shale bands	26.0
Black shales with thin sandstones	2.0
Sharply defined sandstones with abundant siltstones and shales	20.0
Massive sandstone with large load-casts and flute-casts	2.5
Massive hard sandstones	30.0
Shales with thin ironstone bands	1.0
Mudstones with thin sandstones	15.0
Hard greyish green sandstone with iron oxide segregations	1.5
Sandstone	3.0
Black shales with thin sandstones and thin ironstones	1.0
Silty shales showing slumps	3.5
Well-bedded sandstones	9.0
Massive sandstone	2.5
Sandstone	4.2
Top of Longpeak Shale	

The upper 40 m of the section can be examined in more detail at the cliff base between northings [1627] and [1623]:

	Thickness m
Base of Tom's Cove Shale	
Sandstone	5.6
Thin sandstones with laminated siltstones	0.8
Laminated shales	0.8
Massive hard sandstone	5.6
Silty mudstones with some sandy bands; slumped bed at 1.5 m above base	7.0
Sandstone	4.0
Black laminated shales	2.4
Mostly sandstones up to 5 m thick, locally wedge-bedded with hard greyish green conglomerate of sandstone and shale fragments at the base	13.6

The Tom's Cove Shale is repeated at the cliff base by folding at northings [1622], [1590], [1576] and [1568]; the following section is at northing [1622]:

	Thickness m
Hard, black to dark grey silty shales	1.2
Black sulphurous shales containing discoidal concretions at the top and at 0.3 m below the top	0.9
Dark grey slaty shales	0.3
Black shales containing abundant coprolites, some up to 20 mm long, especially in the top 0.9 m. A thin sandstone occurs about 1 m from the top, pale grey nodules 1.4 m from the top and thin sandstones 0.5 m from the base	2.6
Laminated siltstones and mudstones with a few sandstones up to 0.15 m	0.8

Lovell (1965) recorded a similar sequence 5.7 m thick at northing [1590].

The Saturday's Pit Shale is repeated a number of times by folding, and crops out on the foreshore at [1991 1612]. It comprises 5.3 m of grey and black shales, the top 2 m containing coprolites. An impersistent sandstone 2 m below the top contains breccia composed of laminated carbonate concretions. The shales below are greyer and more silty than those above. Other sections in these shales occur at the cliff base at northings [1599], [1542], [1525] and [1519].

A sequence including the Tom's Cove Shale and the Saturday's Pit Shale occurs between northings [1638] and [1608]:

	Thickness m
Shales	6.8
Mainly sandstones	19.0
Saturday's Pit Shale. Black shales with coprolites 2 m overlying impersistent sandstone with breccia of laminated concretions at its base, on black shales	5.3
Thin-bedded sandstones becoming thicker and more massive downwards; bottom sandstone 10.8 m thick	30.4
Sandy slumped bed	2.3
Sandstone, beds up to 0.4 m thick	3.2
Black shales	1.0
Massive sandstone	4.0
Coarsely laminated silty sandstones	4.8
Sandstone in beds up to 1 m thick	4.8
Contorted black shales with nodular layer 1.2 m above base. Coprolites from 2.2 m below top to 0.5 m above base	5.0
Sandstones	5.6
Thin sandstones with laminated siltstones	0.8
Laminated shales	0.8
Hard massive sandstone	5.6
Silty mudstone with some sandy bands. Slumping 1.5 m above base	7.0
Sandstone	4.0
Black laminated shales	2.4
Mostly sandstones up to 5 m thick; hard greyish green conglomerate of sandstone and shale fragments at base. Some wedge-bedding in sandstones	13.6
Dark grey silty shales	1.5
Medium to thick-bedded sandstones	11.0
Dark grey silty shales with thin sandstones 0.8 m below the top and thin ironstone seams	3.2
Mostly sandstones, some up to 3 m thick, with ferruginous segregations	17.6
Slumped bed	2.2
Hard greyish green sandstones with ferruginous segregations	over 14.3
Massive greyish green poorly bedded sandstone	8.0
Thin-bedded sandstones; intervening shales abundant towards top of sequence	14.4

	Thickness m
Silty shales	1.5
Thickly bedded sandstones	18.9
Tom's Cove Shale. Black shales. Thin sandstone 3 m below top. Band of concretions 4 m below top	6.0
Well-bedded sandstones up to 1 m thick, with shales	16.4
Massive sandstone with ferruginous segregations	3.0

Strata between the Saturday's Pit Shale and the Sandy Mouth Shale crop out in folds south of a NW–SE fault at Higher Sharpnose Point, and the following four successions are of these beds. The first lies between northings [1482] and [1470]:

	Thickness m
Mostly sandstones	17.2
Slumped bed	6.0
Massive sandstones with iron oxide segregations	10.0
Silty mudstones and muddy sandstones passing down into banded muddy siltstones	19.8
Massive sandstones, generally about 1 m thick, with iron oxide segregations; some thicker sandstones near base	15.0
Siltstones and mudstones with slumped bed, mainly of shaly debris, near base	12.9
Shales with ironstone bands	2.5
Well-bedded sandstones, some up to 1 m thick, with small load-casts and flute-casts and iron oxide segregations	51.6
Shales	6.0
Slumped bed	7.5
Sandstones	12.0

The second is between northings [1420] and [1413]:

	Thickness m
Massive sandstone with large load-casts	9.9
Well-bedded sandstones with flute-casts and load-casts	4.5
Siltstones with 1-m sandstone near base and 3-m slumped bed at top	6.0
Black silty shales with scattered thin sandstones and thin ironstone bands	14.0
Sandstones	4.8
Massive sandstone with vermiform load-casts	8.0
Thinly bedded (0.2 to 0.3 m) sandstones	7.1
Massive sandstones pinching out to the east	4.5
Thinly bedded sandstones with groove-casts	3.2
Massive sandstone pinching out laterally	3.0
Siltstones and shales	9.0
Massive sandstone	3.0

The third is between northings [1410] and [1392]:

	Thickness m
Laminated cross-bedded sandstone with iron oxide segregations	4.0
Black shales	4.0
Thinly bedded silty sandstones with slumped mudstone at top	9.0
Slumped bed	1.6
Black shales	1.9
Sandstones and shales	8.3
Shales and thin sandstones	1.9
Massive sandstone with some shale	3.0
Thinly bedded sandstones and shales	2.0
Hard massive greyish green sandstones up to 3 m thick; some thinner bedded with siltstone layers; wedge-bedding in channels; flute-casts common	15.0
Dark grey silty shales	5.0
Sandstone with iron oxide segregations	2.0
Sandstones and mudstones	3.8
Shales and mudstones with ironstone seams	4.0

	Thickness m
Sandstone	1.8
Grey laminated mudstones with some thin sandstones	1.4
Sandstones	3.0
Thin sandstones and striped mudstones	1.9
Sandstones up to 1 m thick with slumped masses of black shale with ironstone seams	4.0
Sandstones	1.0

The fourth succession of strata between the Saturday's Pit Shale and the Sandy Mouth Shale lies between Hippa Rock, northing [1372], and the Sandy Mouth Shale at northing [1334]:

	Thickness m
Base of Sandy Mouth Shale	
Sandstones up to 0.8 m thick, commonly flaggy, with few intervening shales	41.9
Very thickly bedded sandstones, with some thin sandstones and rather sheared shales	10.8
Well-bedded sandstones, some flaggy, some hard and up to 0.4 m thick; small load-casts; shales and siltstones common	24.8
Black shales with thin sandstones, some dark grey and muddy; thin ironstones; some signs of slumping	7.0
Mainly sandstones up to 0.5 m thick	10.0
Massive sandstones up to 1 m thick with large load-casts	3.4
Mostly thinly bedded yellowish brown sandstones with interbedded siltstones	8.0
Massive sandstone; some lamination; cross-bedding with foresets up to 0.2 m long	5.0
Mostly thinly bedded sandstones	2.8
Sandstone	1.0
Black shales with some thin sandstones	7.0
Thinly bedded sandstones	3.8
Sheared black shales	6.0
Well-bedded yellowish brown poorly laminated sandstone; some flaggy sandstones and a little intervening shale and siltstone	18.9
Shales and silty mudstones with some sandstone	5.4
Slumped bed	2.0
Black shales with ironstone seams	6.5
Soft massive sandstones with large iron oxide pods	5.0
Very thinly bedded striped sandstones, showing ripple-drift and cross-bedding	2.5
Massive sandstones of variable thickness; some flaggy, striped siltstones	4.8
Black shales with thin ironstones	6.5
Massive sandstones	4.0
Silty mudstones	2.5
Sandstone	1.0
Shales	1.3
Dark grey shales with a 20-mm sandstone	1.0
Thinly bedded rather flaggy sandstones	8.0
Sandstone	1.4
Black shales	2.5
Sandstone	2.0
Banded black shales	2.5
Sandstone	3.0
Black shales with thin ironstones	3.0
Well-bedded sandstones; top sandstone over 1 m thick	3.9
Sandstone showing internal channelling	1.5
Black shales	1.5
Well-bedded sandstone	1.0
Black shales	1.2
Thinly bedded sandstones, some flaggy, with a few beds up to 1.5 m thick; interbedded silty shales	18.5
Sandstone	1.0
Striped siltstones and shales	1.5
Sandstones up to 1 m thick	6.0
Slaty shales	1.5

The Sandy Mouth Shale is much folded between Stanbury Mouth, northing [1340], and Lower Sharpnose Point, northing [1270]. It is vertical at northing [1334] and apparently 12.9 m thick, but much folded and sheared. One, possibly two, seams of laminated carbonate concretions at this locality have yielded *Anthracoceratoides cornubiensis*, *Caneyella sp.*, *Dunbarella sp.* and palaeoniscid scales. At northing [1287] the strata are less deformed, and 8 m of sulphurous black shales with laminated concretions contain a 0.3-m sandstone 1 m from the top; a similar fauna has been recorded.

Lower Sharpnose Point to Warren Gutter

Strata between the Sandy Mouth Shale and the Warren Gutter Shale crop out between a NW–SE fault at northing [1275] and a landslip at northing [1234]:

	Thickness m
Mostly thick sandstones	23.4
Slumped bed	2.0
Well-bedded sandstone	2.3
Slumped bed	8.3
Shales with ironstone bands	1.5
Sandstone	0.8
Silty shales with thin sandstones, passing down into black shales with ironstones	3.0
Sandstone	2.6
Shales	1.2
Sandstone	0.9
Black silty shales	1.0
Thinly bedded sandstones	2.0
Sandstones up to 1.5 m thick, with iron oxide segregations in load-casts	7.9
Silty mudstones	2.2
Sandstone	1.5
Sandstones up to 1.5 m thick with thin sandstones and shales	7.4
Sandstones up to 1 m thick with iron oxide segregations and internal load-casts	4.1
Slumped bed	about 8.0
Dark grey shales with ironstone bands; 0.5-m sandstone in middle of sequence	2.2
Hard sandstones	5.0
Shales and thin sandstones	4.2
Massive sandstone	6.0
Sandstones in units up to 1 m thick; some laminated siltstones	11.0
Sandstone	3.0
Black shales with ironstone	2.0
Sandstones with iron oxide segregations	4.0
Well-bedded sandstones with shales and mudstones; scattered sandstones up to 1.5 m thick with iron oxide segregations	27.7
Shales with thin sandstones	7.2
Well-bedded sandstones, some flaggy, with a 0.4-m slumped band 4 m from the top	15.4
Massive sandstone	5.0
Black shales, some silty, with slumped bed at top	7.0
Hard greyish green sandstones	5.0
Sandstones up to 0.5 m thick with abundant shales and laminated siltstones; some iron-stained sandstone; sporadic shale bands up to 1 m thick	17.9
Sandstone	1.5
Thinly bedded sandstone	2.0
Massive sandstone	2.0
Sandstones up to 1 m thick with some shales	9.9
Mudstones containing 0.5 m of thinly bedded sandstones	2.5
Thickly bedded and massive sandstones	18.0
Slumped bed	13.2
Massive sandstones	6.2
Thinly bedded sandstones, some beds up to 0.4 m thick; shale beds common, particularly at the top	12.9
Dark grey shales with some sandstone bands at 4 m above the base	12.5
Sandstone	0.5
Silty mudstones with thin brown sandy bands	5.9
Shaly mudstones with thin sandstones; mud-pellet conglomerate at top	2.5
Well-bedded sandstones up to 0.8 m thick, with some shaly beds	7.0
Sandstones; basal bed 2 m thick	14.0
Hard greyish green sandstone with flute-casts on the base	4.0
Banded silty mudstone and muddy siltstone with graded sandstone beds	7.8
Sandstone	2.3
Shales	7.0
Sandstone	1.5
Slumped bed	4.0
Sandstone	5.0

The following succession lies between an anticline at northing [1228] and the Warren Gutter Shale at northing [1204]:

	Thickness m
Base of Warren Gutter Shale	
Sandstone	1.0
Laminated siltstones and mudstones with thin turbiditic sandstones	4.0
Muddy siltstones, banded towards the base, with many wisps of sand; slumped bed towards the top	10.0
Sheared massive greenish grey sandstone	9.8
Slumped bed passing down into banded siltstones and mudstones with evenly spaced sandstone bands	3.0
Banded siltstones and mudstones	2.0
Shales with some sandstones towards the top	12.8
Sandstone	0.5
Shales and thin sandstones	3.8
Massive sandstone	2.0
Medium-bedded sandstone	2.0
Shales and thin sandstones, passing down into shales	5.3
Slumped bed	1.0
Slaty shale	3.0
Slumped bed	18.0
Poorly exposed sandstones with shales	13.0
Dark grey shales with slumped bed near base	26.3
Medium-bedded sandstones	18.8
[*Fault*]	
Silty mudstone with interbedded sandstones, one bearing a sand volcano	9.0
Sandstone	1.0
Dark silty mudstones passing up into black shales	18.0
Well-bedded and laminated sandstones	2.0
Shales with thin sandstones	4.5
Black shales with ironstone bands	9.0
Sharply defined turbiditic sandstones with shales	12.0

The following succession lies between a fault at northing [1198] and an anticline at northing [1162]:

	Thickness m
Dark grey shales with slumped bed, siltstones and some sandstones	6.6
Thin sandstones and shales	2.2
Laminated shales with thin sandstones at the base	10.0
Hard greyish green sandstone with a laminated shale bed 2 m from the base	4.0

	Thickness m
Slumped bed overlain by shales and laminated sandstones	1.0
Laminated black shales and thin sandstones	2.4
Slumped bed	2.0
Laminated black shales	4.3
Slumped bed	2.0
Thin sandstones and shales	1.0
Sandstone	2.5
Shales with thin sandstones about 0.3 m thick	3.0
Massive sandstone with iron oxide segregations and internal load-casts	7.0
Dark grey shales, with some 50-mm sandstones at the top	19.4
Hard well-bedded sandstones with iron oxide segregations and mudstone pellet layers	4.5
Hard sharply bedded sandstones up to 1 m thick, with shales	13.5
Massive sandstone	7.0
Black shales with some thinly bedded sandstones near the top; sheared at the top	11.1
Massive sheared sandstone	4.0
Slumped bed	seen

The cliffs between northings [1148] and [1131] contain the following succession:

	Thickness m
Sandstones in beds over 1 m thick	8.6
Massive sandstone	1.5
Hard, grey slumped mudstone	1.5
Slaty laminated shale and mudstone with slumped masses of silty sandstone; some thin sandstone bands at the base	13.0
Laminated silty sandstones with thin sandstones	3.0
Massive sandstone with iron oxide segregations	1.3
Thin sandstones and shales	2.5
Hard greyish green sandstone, fractured, possibly with some repetition	7.0
Sheared black shales with thin sandstones	1.0
Hard greyish green sandstone, with load-casts and a mud-flake conglomerate at the base	4.0
Hard greyish green sandstone	1.5
Black shales with thin sandstones towards the middle of the sequence	6.3
Contorted thin sandstones and shales	6.0
Sandstones up to 0.5 m thick with shales, in core of fold	4.0

The Warren Gutter Shale is repeated within a complex synclinorium and crops out in the cliff [2016 1204] north of Duckpool, where it is about 8 m thick and associated with a slumped bed. Better exposures occur at Warren Gutter, on the foreshore [2002 1106] and in the cliff behind. The thickness of the shale is somewhat exaggerated by folding and shearing but is about 10 m, with a band of laminated carbonate concretions about 7 m from the top. Folded into the base of the Warren Gutter Shale are hard, pale grey sandstones resembling those of the Crackington Formation. Concretions within shales on the foreshore [2005 1108] yielded *Rhabdoderma sp.* and palaeoniscid scales. A further band of nodules in the cliff [2013 1099] has yielded '*Anthracoceras*' *hindi* and *Gastrioceras depressum*, together with *Dunbarella macgregori*, *Caneyella sp.*, and an orthocone nautiloid. This assemblage provides a correlation with the '*Anthracoceras*' *aegiranum* horizon. Strata above the Warren Gutter Shale occur within the cores of two synclines, one at northing [1200] and the other at northing [1100]. They consist chiefly of medium-bedded sandstones along with some shales.

Warren Gutter to Sandy Mouth

Strata between the Sandy Mouth Shale and the Warren Gutter Shale are exposed between northings [1095] and [1009]. Sections are as follows:

Northing [1095] to northing [1078].

	Thickness m
Base of Warren Gutter Shale	
Laminated siltstones and shales, passing down into siltstones and silty mudstones with thin brown laminated and cross-laminated sandstones; sheared sandstones 2.3 m, 4 m and 6 m below the top	7.0
Laminated mudstones and muddy siltstones with brown sandstone bands; more shaly in depth	20.0
Silty mudstones and silty shales, slumped	1.0
Laminated shales with thin sandstones	5.2
Very hard greyish green massive sandstones with a few internal load-casts and rust-stained segregations	18.0
Dark grey shales with thin sandstones at the top	9.0
Massive greyish brown sandstones up to 0.9 m thick with flute-casts and load-casts; mud-pellet conglomerate at base	6.0
Slumped bed; abundant sandstone clasts at base	5.0
Well-bedded sandstones up to 2 m thick, with shale partings becoming more common towards the base	9.5
Shales with thin sandstones	1.0
Sandstone	0.6
Colour-banded dark grey shales with some thin sandstones, ironstone bands and scattered ironstone nodules	12.0
Sandstones with laminated siltstones	1.5
Laminated siltstone; silty shales near middle of sequence; thin sandstones near base	9.9
Hard massive rust-stained sandstone with large flute-casts and load-casts on the base	5.0
Black shales	1.0
Sandstones, thinly bedded at the top	1.5
Black shales with ironstone bands	3.0
Flaggy, laminated siltstones and silty sandstones	1.8
Well-bedded sandstones	4.5

Northing [1071] to northing [1048]

	Thickness m
Shales	4.2
Medium-bedded sandstones	6.6
Black shales	3.1
Well-bedded sandstones up to 0.4 m thick	4.9
Slumped mudstones with sandy bands showing tight non-tectonic folds	3.0
Massive sandstone	2.0
Thinly bedded sandstones with shales	1.7
Black shales	1.5
Thickly and thinly bedded sandstones	3.7
Black shales	1.0
Massive sandstones with abundant shale bands	9.0
[*No exposure*]	1.7
Black shales	4.0
[*Small NW–SE dextral wrench fault*]	
Massive sandstone	8.0
Thick sandstones and shales	4.7
Black shales	4.6
Thinly to medium-bedded sandstones with shales	20.0
Shales	0.8
Medium-bedded sandstones	2.4
Shales with thin sandstones and thin ironstone bands	4.6
Laminated sandstones and siltstones with ripple-drift lamination; some sandstones up to 0.3 m thick	8.0
Sandstone	1.5
Soft, pale-grey-weathering sandstones 50 mm to 1.5 m thick, with wedge-bedding and flute-casts	6.4
Slumped bed	4.0
Thinly bedded sandstones	4.0
Massive sandstone	5.0

	Thickness m
Slumped bed	2.0
Sandstone	2.4
Slumped bed	6.0
Sandstone	4.0
Slumped bed	7.0
Sandstones	2.1
Black shales	2.0
Sandstones up to 1 m thick	10.1
Black shales	2.5
Slumped bed	6.5
Massive and thinly bedded sandstones	61.1

Northing [1048] to northing [1034]

	Thickness m
Black shales	2.0
Thickly bedded sandstones with 0.8 m of shales midway up sequence	21.0
Shales	3.0
Massive slumped bed	17.0
Medium-bedded sandstones	4.8
Shales	0.3
Thick sandstones with some thinly bedded sandstones	14.5
Thinly bedded sandstones	6.3
Black shales	0.4
Sandstone	1.0
Sandstones up to 0.5 m thick with some thinly bedded sandstones; abundant load-casts	19.5
Sandstone	1.0
Sandstones in beds about 2.5 m thick	8.2

Northing [1033] to northing [1020]

	Thickness m
Shales	3.8
Mainly sandstones	21.0
Shales	2.0
Medium-bedded sandstones	3.1
Sandstone	1.5
Medium-bedded sandstones	1.6
Massive sandstones with many internal load-casts, some vermiform	8.0
Shaly mudstones with some thin sandstones	2.0
Well-bedded sandstones	8.0
Black shales with many sandstone beds up to 0.2 m thick	3.0
Slumped bed	8.0
Medium to thinly bedded sandstones	2.7
Shales	0.2
Thinly bedded sandstones	2.7
Massive sandstone	1.0
Medium to thinly bedded sandstones	2.9
Massive sandstone	1.5
Sandstone with a slumped siltstone bed	0.7
Thinly bedded to medium-bedded sandstones	2.2
Shales	0.3
Sandstone	1.5
Medium-bedded sandstones	1.3
Thinly bedded sandstones	2.2
Sandstone	1.0
Thinly bedded sandstones with siltstones	6.0
Disrupted black shales with 20-mm sandy bands; some tectonic repetition	about 8.3
Sheared mudstones	4.6
Black shales	about 10.0

NW–SE wrench fault at northing [1020] to northing [1009]

	Thickness m
Massive slumped bed	about 20.0
Black shales	1.5
Sandy slumped bed	4.0
Shales	7.0
Well-bedded pale-grey-weathering sandstones	5.6
Massive sandstones with a 2-m banded sandstone 10 m above the base	13.0
Medium-bedded sandstones	11.4
Black shales with 20-mm sandstone bands	1.5
Medium-bedded sandstones	9.1
Black shales with many thin sandstones up to 0.2 m thick	12.5
Thinly bedded sandstones with abundant mudstone	3.6
Laminated sandstones	1.0
Massive mudstone	1.5
Laminated sandstones	1.0
Medium- to thinly bedded sandstones	6.0
Laminated siltstones and sandstones showing ripple-drift cross-lamination; burrowed at the top	2.6
Medium-bedded sandstones; beds up to 2.5 m thick	19.8

Top of Sandy Mouth Shale

The Sandy Mouth Shale is repeated three times by folding around Sandy Mouth. At northing [1009] it is between 6 and 7 m thick and has yielded *Caneyella sp.* and anthracoceratids. At northing [1000] the Sandy Mouth Shale has a structurally expanded thickness; around 17 m of black shales are striped with silty bands and contain a hard grey sandstone at 4.5 m below the top. Discoidal laminated concretions are well developed at 4 m above the base and less well developed at 5 m. The shales and nodules have yielded *Caneyella sp., Dunbarella sp., Anthracoceratoides cornubiensis* and fish remains. At northing [0988] much of the shale sequence has been sheared out.

Sandy Mouth to Bude

Strata between the Saturday's Pit Shale and the Sandy Mouth Shale are exposed between northings [0956] and [0909], much affected by folding and faulting. Representative successions are as follows:

Northing [0956] to northing [0944]

	Thickness m
Massive, rather brecciated sandstone	8.0
Dark grey shales with thin ironstone bands	1.7
Massive sandstone	3.5
Laminated silty sandstones	2.0
[*Fault parallel to bedding*]	
Laminated mudstones and siltstones, possibly a slumped bed	0.9
Laminated siltstones	0.9
Massive sandstones up to 1 m thick	4.0
Medium-bedded sandstones	3.5
Massive sandstone	1.6
Disturbed sandstones and shales	9.4
Thickly bedded and massive sandstones	3.2
Black shales with laminated sandstones	1.7
Sandstone	1.4
Laminated siltstones, mudstones and some shales with thin sandstones	4.3
Medium-bedded sandstones	1.7
Silty sandstones and mudstones	1.6
Massive sandstone	2.4
Thinly bedded sandstones	2.6
Poorly bedded sandstone with large load-casts	1.9

	Thickness m
Disturbed siltstones, with some laminated and cross-laminated layers	1.0
Massive sandstones up to 0.4 m thick with laminated siltstones and mudstones	8.0
Massive sandstones, one showing flute-casts	7.8
Sandstones up to 0.3 m thick with interbedded mudstones	8.4
Mudstones with sandy bands	1.8
Laminated silty mudstones with some sandstone at the top	4.2
Sandstone	1.2
Mudstones with thin sandstones	1.5
Sandstones with interbedded mudstones	4.3

Northing [0926] to northing [0909]

	Thickness m
Massive sandstones in beds up to 3 m thick with bands of muddy siltstone; black shale clasts at the bases of some of the sandstones	13.2
Thinly bedded soft, pale-grey-weathering sandstones	1.7
Dark grey silty shales; many soft muddy sandstones 50 mm to 0.25 m thick, showing cross-lamination; thin ironstone bands near top	1.7
Sandstone	1.0
Well-bedded soft pale-grey-weathering sandstones with some beds containing clasts of dark grey shale at their bases	1.1
Silty shales, laminated siltstones and thin sandstones	1.3
Pale grey laminated siltstones, with thin sandstones bearing load-casts; sandy silty slumped bed at top	1.4
[Small fault]	
Sandstones	3.0
Siltstones and silty shales	3.4
Massive sandstones in three beds	5.0
Dark grey shales with thin ironstone seams	1.3
Massive sandstones up to 1 m thick	3.0
Dark grey shales	0.6
Silty laminated sandstones	2.3
Massive sandstone	2.5
Silty mudstones	1.5
Sandstone	1.7
Thinly bedded sandstones with shaly layers in middle of sequence	4.0
Shales with detached load-casts	2.0
Shales	0.6
Sharply bedded sandstones, some showing channelling and laminated horizons; scattered thicker massive sandstones showing load-casts and some shaly horizons; 2-m sandstone at base	11.2
Thinly bedded sandstones with abundant shales	7.4
Mainly sandstones, up to 1 m thick	20.0
Top of Saturday's Pit Shale	

The Saturday's Pit Shale north of Northcott Mouth, at northing [0896], comprises 3.3 m of black sulphurous shales, with thin sandy bands and ironstone seams in the top half of the sequence. A band of laminated carbonate concretions lies at 0.6 m above the base, and lensoid ironstone concretions at 0.9 m. Further laminated carbonate concretions 20 to 30 mm across are scattered between 0.3 and 1.6 m from the top, and coprolitic pellets occur between 0.1 and 1.5 m from the top. Nodules from these shales have yielded fish remains including acanthodian scales. More southerly exposures of the Saturday's Pit Shale, at northings [0750] and [0730], show 3.66 m and 3 m of shales respectively with concretions about 1 m above the bases. At Saturday's Pit, northing [0682], 3.96 m of shales contain thin cross-laminated sandstones about 1.52 m above the base and laminated concretions up to 0.15 m across at 0.9 m above the base; the nodules have yielded the remains of *Cornuboniscus*

budensis. The Saturday's Pit Shale is repeated at the cliff base by folding at northings [0909], [0742], [0693] and [0682].

Beds between the Tom's Cove Shale and the Saturday's Pit Shale are exposed between northings [0895] and [0670] in the following sections:

Strata below Saturday's Pit Shale south of West Park Pit at northing [0895] to core of box-shaped anticline at Menachurch Point at northing [0880]:

	Thickness m
Base of Saturday's Pit Shale	
Well-bedded sandstones up to 0.2 m thick	3.6
Sandstones up to 0.35 m thick with load-casts on bases and ripple-drift lamination on tops; an interbedded thin shale band contains a 20-mm sandstone bearing small groove-casts and prod-casts, and indistinct goniatite bounce-casts	4.6
Banded dark grey to black shales; thin sandstones and slumped bed at top	2.0
Thinly bedded sharply defined sandstones with interbedded grey shales	2.3
Soft greenish grey sandstones up to 1 m thick, many showing cross-lamination and interbedded siltstones and mudstones	9.0
Massive sandstone	4.7
Slumped bed	3.0
Thin sandstones with shales	1.5
Massive sandstone	1.9
Massive sandstones up to 1 m thick; some shales and thin sandstones	6.1
Thin sandstones with shales and banded siltstones	5.2
Massive sandstones up to 1 m thick with load-casts and ripple-marks; some bands of laminated sandstone	10.7
Massive sandstone	2.0
Shales with thin sandstones	1.5
Thinly bedded sandstones	2.0
Massive sandstone	2.0
Shales with thin sandstones	3.0
Massive sandstones	1.9
Black papery shales (probably top of Tom's Cove Shale)	3.0

Northing [0871] to northing [0860] (Northcott Mouth):

	Thickness m
Massive pale grey sandstones	6.3
Siltstones	1.5
Massive sandstones in beds 0.6 to 0.9 m thick	6.0
Shales, with sandstones up to 0.1 m thick	1.0
Massive sandstones	4.3
Medium-bedded sandstones	2.3
Black shales with thin sandstones and thin ironstones	1.7
Massive sandstones in beds up to 0.6 m thick	8.7
Shales with thin sandstones	2.8
Thinly bedded sandstones	5.5
Shales with scattered 0.1-m sandstones	1.2
Sandstones in beds 1 to 2 m thick showing some lamination; carbonaceous layers towards top; some ripple-drift bedding; large load-casts on bedding plane near base	9.3
Black silty mudstones	0.9
Thinly bedded sandstones	1.7
Blocky, silty mudstones	0.9
Well-bedded, laminated sandstone with some cross-bedding with foresets about 0.25 m long; rust-stained band in middle of sequence	2.5
Silty sandstones and sandy mudstones	0.6
Massive structureless sandstone containing dark grey ellipsoid stained with iron oxide	1.7
Soft carious-weathered sandstone, cross-laminated towards	

Thickness
m

the top, with load-casts, foundered load-casts and vertical
sand bodies; some worm burrows and disrupted black shale
fragments; plant debris common in mid part of sandstone   3.2

Flaggy siltstones and sandstones at northing [0751], a few metres
below the Saturday's Pit Shale, contain xiphosurid tracks. A
succession between northings [0771] and [0750] is repeated in the
following section.

Strata beneath the Saturday's Pit Shale between Saturday's Pit
Swimming Pool, at northing [0682], and northing [0670]:

Thickness
m

Base of Saturday's Pit Shale

Massive greenish grey sandstones 0.31 to 1.2 m thick with a few intervening shaly bands up to 1 m thick	7.62
Sandstones and shales	3.0
Massive greenish grey sandstones with a few irregular lenses of grey sandstone	1.7
Black shales	0.02
Massive greenish grey sandstone	1.4
Black silty shales	0.1
Cross-bedded sandstone	0.1
Black shales	0.3
Greenish grey sandstone with ripple-drift cross-lamination at top	0.2
Grey siltstones	0.1
Grey siltstones with slumped sandy beds	0.2
Grey laminated siltstones with some plant fragments	0.5
Massive greenish grey sandstones in three beds separated by shales up to 20 mm thick	1.3
Current-bedded sandstones alternating with black silty shales in beds up to 0.1 m thick	1.0
Grey sandy siltstones with comminuted plant fragments and three pale grey slumped sandstone bands	0.5
Black shales with graded silty sandstones up to 20 mm thick	0.5
Massive sandstone with load-casts and flame-structures on base	2.4
Slumped bed of banded siltstone and green silty sandstone	0.2
Massive grey sandstone	seen

Beds below the Tom's Cove Shale are exposed also between the
core of an anticline at northing [0780] and Maer High Cliff at
northing [0772]. They are steeply dipping or vertical and consist
mainly of medium-bedded sandstones with two major massive
sandstone units, one at northing [0777] and the other at northing
[0773]. The sequence contains several bands of dark grey to black
shales up to 4.25 m thick of which the lowest, at northing [0779],
is about 4 m thick and contains a 1-m sandstone from which
irregular protrusions of sandstone extend into the overlying shales.

The Tom's Cove Shale at northing [0772], near Maer High Cliff,
comprises 7.5 m of black shales and mudstones. Ironstone nodules
occur 1 m from the base, a band of carbonate concretions up to
0.4 m across at 1.5 m, and coprolitic pellets between 3 and 3.7 m. A
thin sandstone lies near the top of the sequence. Other exposures of
these shales occur at Curtis's Rock [2019 0859] where a single
laminated concretion has been recorded, in synclinal cores at the
cliff top at northings [0826] and [0816], and on the foreshore near
Bude Haven, at northing [0654], where nodules have yielded
pyritised fish remains.   E C F

Hole Rock [2215 2262] *to Brownspear Beach* [2240 2340]

The base of the Bude Formation is taken at the base of the thick
sandstone which lies immediately above the Hartland Quay Shale
and forms Hole Rock. The succession to the north contains sporadic
thick sandstones of Bude Formation type and is truncated at the
northern end of Brownspear Beach by two major strike faults with

southerly downthrows. The Longpeak Shale crops out about 33 m
above the base of the succession just north of Hole Rock and is
repeated by successive folds northwards to Longpeak [2211 2301].

A thick sequence of siltstones with thin sandstones beneath the
Longpeak Shale is similar to that found at this horizon to the north
(Edmonds, Williams and Taylor, 1979), but is much reduced to the
south near Litter Mouth [2071 1691]. On Longpeak Beach [2218
2278], in the southern limb of an anticline exposed on the foreshore, a group of four thick sandstones is channelled into the top of
these siltstones. The sandstones are repeated to the south by
folding. In the northern exposure the thick sandstones die out to
the east and pass into thin sandstones to the west. The channel
appears to trend approximately NNW–SSE.

A shale horizon 1.2 m thick and 40 m above the Longpeak Shale
carries fusiform coprolite pellets, and it is probably this horizon
that crops out at the top of Sandhole Cliff [2213 2090]. This shale
is found in a similar position above the Longpeak Shale near
Hartland Point (Edmonds, Williams and Taylor, 1979). A similar
shale is exposed in the cliff between the two strike faults at
Brownspear Beach, suggesting that the main movement was on the
more northerly of the two faults.

Details of the succession between Brownspear Beach and Hole
Rock are as follows:

Thickness
m

Thinly bedded sandstones with silty partings	0.84
Slumped bed, dark grey silty mudstone with contorted sandstone clasts	3.43
Laminated siltstones with thin laminated sandstones	1.75
Thinly bedded sandstones interbedded with siltstones	4.88
Thinly and medium-bedded sandstones interbedded with siltstones	3.15
Fine-grained sandstones with silty partings, passing laterally into a composite thick sandstone	4.37
Black shales with thin silty laminae; 0.5 m of thin sandstones near top	2.49
Thinly bedded sandstones, some interbedded with siltstones	5.56
Black laminated shales with sideritic bands	1.07
Laminated siltstones with some ripple-drift cross-bedded sandy bands; thin sandstones at top and near base	4.60
Thinly and medium-bedded sandstones, some interbedded with siltstones, some with silty partings	17.07
Black laminated shales with fusiform coprolite pellets	1.22
Thinly laminated siltstones and thin sandstones	0.89
Dark grey laminated mudstones, partly slumped	0.99
Thin sandstones, some interbedded with siltstones or with silty partings	7.04
Thinly and medium-bedded sandstones	7.32
Siltstones and thin sandstones	1.22
Three composite medium-bedded sandstones	1.90
Thin sandstones and siltstones	1.07
Composite sandstone beds	1.22
Thin sandstones with silty partings	0.61
Two composite medium-bedded sandstones	1.68
Thinly bedded sandstones with some silty partings	2.67
Sandstones 0.86 and 1.58 m thick	2.44
Thinly and medium-bedded sandstones interbedded with some siltstone	5.56

The section above was measured down to the top of the Longpeak
Shale at Longpeak. The continuation below was measured down
from the top of the Longpeak Shale at Hole Rock.

Thickness
m

Black shales with silty and sideritic bands 10 to 20 mm thick and scattered fusiform coprolite pellets	0.86
Laminated and ripple-drift cross-bedded sandstone with aggregates of fusiform pellets in load-casts on base	0.30

Longpeak Shale. Black shales with silty and sideritic bands, underlain by dark grey and black silty laminated shales with calcareous nodules in the basal 0.56 m containing goniatite spat; some nodules concreted around plant fragments; fossils include *Caneyella sp.* and fish remains [2213 2303], mollusc spat and fish remains including an acanthodian spine [2229 2272], and *Calamites sp.*, *Caneyella sp.* and indeterminate juvenile goniatites [2228 2272]   2.23

	Thickness m
Dark grey siltstones, with sporadic sandstones 50 to 100 mm thick	3.25
Thin sandstones with silty partings	1.96
Siltstones with laminae 25 to 50 mm thick	2.74
Thin flaggy sandstones and siltstones	0.86
Thin sandstones with silty partings, becoming silty and laminated laterally and apparently channelled into underlying siltstones	2.44
Flaggy, sandy-banded siltstones passing down into flaggy sandstones 50 to 150 mm thick	5.79
Thinly and medium-bedded sandstones with silty partings	1.37
Sandstone beds 1.02 and 1.14 m thick separated by 0.38 m of laminated sandstones and siltstones	2.54
Thinly and medium-bedded sandstones with interbedded siltstones 50 to 150 mm thick; thin ripple-drift cross-bedded sandstones beneath	2.90
Sandstone with load-casts and flute-casts on base	1.02
Laminated or graded dark grey siltstones 25 to 100 mm thick	0.76
Thinly and medium-bedded sandstones with silty partings	5.66
Thick composite sandstone laminated in upper part	2.74

This section is continuous with that for the Crackington Formation south of Hole Rock (pp. 19–20).   RTT

Inland exposures

Morwenstow to Ashmansworthy

A quarry [2284 1411] south of Shop shows black shales 3 m, overlain by massive brown feldspathic sandstone with large load-casts 15.2 m and thickly bedded sandstones with flaggy sandstones and shales 6 m. The massive sandstone is similar to one on the coast at northing [1416]. The stream adjacent to this quarry has exposed massive sandstones, and also 6 m of siltstones [2349 1386]. A stream [2443 1527 to 2442 1627] south-east of Gooseham shows mainly sandstones, but 3 m of shales crop out at [2432 1594]. A small quarry [2432 1588] shows 6 m of shales with thin sandstones, with a band of subspherical concretions towards the top of the section, and from its position along strike from the coast it is probable that the shales are either the Tom's Cove Shale or the Saturday's Pit Shale.

East of the watershed between the coastal streams and the River Tamar system exposures are extremely sparse. The Lamberal Water cuts through thinly bedded sandstones [2672 1322 to 2669 1331] and thick sandstones with siltstones [2534 1360]. Farther inland near Hardsworthy shales and thin sandstones with ripple-marked tops are exposed in a stream between [2823 1653] and [2820 1669]; well-bedded sandstones are common in the northern part of this section. Another stream, between [3148 1695] and [3132 1732], shows mainly sandstones; one bed [3144 1714] is 9.2 m thick. A small quarry [3152 1602] south of this stream shows sandstones up to 0.2 m thick with a 0.5-m slumped bed. A small stream to the south-south-east [3162 1562 to 3177 1500] shows mainly sandstones, but locally 4 m of siltstones [3174 1525] and 3 m of silty shales [3179 1512]. Over 7 m of shales and sandstones crop out near Ashmansworthy in a tributary of the River Torridge [3300 1679]. In the bank of the River Torridge [3380 1710] near Ashmansworthy Bridge siltstones and shales contain some sandstones.

Duckpool to Alfardisworthy

Exposures along tracks in Stowe Wood, as between [2125 1154] and [2202 1146], are chiefly of mudstones with micaceous siltstones; massive sandstones occur in places [2202 1147; 2212 1134], as does flaggy greyish green micaceous sandstone [2191 1133]. To the south, shales with thin sandstones are exposed [2142 1134] near Stowe Barton.

A stream section farther east shows mainly shales [2306 1124 to 2311 1135] with small discoidal concretions [2311 1134]. Other thick shaly successions are exposed in streams near Kilkhampton; that between [2377 1175] and [2450 1174] contains discoidal concretions. Many streams east of Kilkhampton show dominantly shales and siltstones, as between [2525 1007] and [2567 1055]. This last stream also cuts through black shales [2629 1157 to 2694 1145] with a band of carbonate concretions [2657 1152; 2670 1153] which have yielded *Anthracoceratites sp.* The fauna is inconclusive but both lithology and the position along strike from the coast point to a correlation with the Sandy Mouth Shale. Farther east towards Tamar Lake, exposures and debris indicate a mainly shaly succession; outcrops in ditches [2785 1025; 2871 2055] yielded small discoidal carbonate concretions which may indicate the presence of the Warren Gutter Shale.

Excavations between [2908 1184] and [2888 1169] for a new reservoir showed the following succession:

	Thickness m
Massive sandstone	1.5
Grey siltstones and silty shales with a thin lenticular sandstone near the base	17.0
Thinly to medium-bedded sandstones and shales	12.0
Sandy slumped bed	18.0
Thinly bedded sandstones with a little interbedded shale	1.0
Massive sandstone	4.2
Argillaceous slumped bed with some bodies of sandstone	5.6
[No exposure]	2.0
Thickly bedded sandstones with terraced load-casts and flute-casts on base	1.0
Siltstones and silty shales with a few thin sandstones	6.0
Massive sandstone	2.5
Shales and siltstones with many sandstones up to 0.5 m thick	5.5

Northcott Mouth to Moreton Mill

A large disused quarry [2315 0895] shows dark grey shales with very thin sandstones 3.7 m, overlain by well-bedded sandstones 24 m, and shales with sandstones up to 0.15 m thick, showing flute-casts and groove-casts on their bases and with plant remains, 24.38 m. Another quarry [2406 0834] exposes well-bedded sandstones and mudstones with some flaggy sandstones. Stream sections show mainly shales [2516 1000 to 2504 0936], thick shales [2505 0928 to 2500 0916], and mainly medium-bedded sandstones [2485 0822 to 2515 0770]. To the east a 60-m-wide outcrop of shales occurs in a stream around [2710 0832] with some thin sandstones and a band of laminated concretions up to 0.2 m across; it probably includes the Tom's Cove Shale. A quarry [2767 0936] east of Lopthorne shows the following succession:

	Thickness m
Hard, greyish green medium-bedded sandstones with scattered linear sole-marks and a few shale bands	7.0
Dark grey shales	1.0
Greenish brown muddy structureless silty sandstone with abundant plant remains, probably a slumped bed	2.5
Medium-bedded sandstone, thinly bedded towards top	3.7
Shales	0.3
Massive sandstones with a few shaly partings	6.0

	Thickness m
Dark grey laminated shales with sporadic 40-mm sandstones near bottom	2.9
Silty shales with scattered thin sandstones	0.7
Muddy sandstones	0.4
Grey silty mudstones	3.1
Dark grey laminated shales	1.4
Medium-bedded and massive sandstones; some traces of internal lamination	4.9
Dark grey silty shales	0.5
Medium-bedded and massive sandstones	1.5
Medium to thinly bedded sandstones with intervening siltstones and mudstones	6.0
Massive sandstone	4.0

Bude to Kingford

The A39 road through Stratton [2270 0629 to 2280 0651] has been cut through Head to expose near-vertical sandstones with a little black shale and siltstone. The sandstones show load-casts and are strongly jointed perpendicular to the bedding; they tend to weather along bedding and joints to develop a spheroidal appearance. A quarry [2276 0634] shows sandstones dipping about 30° N and appears to be separated from the roadside exposures by a fault. Another quarry [2285 0685], now occupied by a garage, shows three greyish green rusty-weathering sandstones 1.2 m, 0.6 m and 0.3 m thick, separated by thinly laminated pale grey siltstones. A road cutting [2307 0712] exposes black fissile shales about 7.6 m thick grading into silty mudstones towards the top. The beds dip about 20° N beneath massive sandstone, and overlie thinly bedded silty sandstones.

East of Stratton, three streams which join near Diddies [236 064] show the following exposures: upstream for 82 m from [2362 0630] mainly black shales dipping 20°–30° W, underlain by thinly laminated pale grey siltstones [2373 0628] and these in turn by massive grey sandstones with subordinate shales; downstream from [2362 0630] massive, poorly-bedded grey sandstones; at [2399 0652] a minor open anticline is in black shales overlying sandstone; between [2358 0648] and [2360 0696] discontinuous exposures of sandstones in beds 0.15 to 0.6 m thick with intervening poorly exposed shales and siltstones.

A stream [2592 0730 to 2570 0673] just west of Grimscott contains almost continuous exposures of mainly thinly to medium-bedded sandstones, with a band of shale possibly 10 to 20 m thick at [2566 0681]. In a nearby stream [2605 0641] siltstones and sandy mudstones appear to form a slumped bed. Excavations [2798 0657] at Burmsdon exposed yellow-weathering flaggy silty sandstones, and farther east, in a small stream near Kingford, very soft yellow-weathering sandstones are exposed [2900 0605].

ECF

Woolfardisworthy to Parkham

A quarry [3403 2119] at Cranford Water shows the following sequence, dipping 65/170°:

	Thickness m
Sandstone, greyish brown massive with bottom-structures	1.20
Shale, grey silty	0.22
Siltstone, grey shaly cross-bedded	0.15
Sandstone	0.75

Fairly coarse-grained greyish brown sandstone 2.5 m thick dips 72°/180° in a roadside exposure [3534 2107] 1 km W of Parkham Ash, and 1.5 m of black shale in the roadside 110 m to the N have a similar dip. This is part of a shale bed traceable for 0.5 km to E and W.

Buckland Brewer–Monkleigh–Weare Giffard

Two adjacent quarries [417 204] in Buckland Brewer are now overgrown, but a nearby stream section [4181 2038] contains 3.5 m of fairly coarse-grained turbiditic sandstone in beds up to 0.2 m thick with thin shaly partings. Farther east, in the valley of the River Duntz, a quarry [4331 2032] shows 1.25 m of massive grey turbiditic sandstone, on 1.20 m of current-bedded shaly siltstones. On the opposite side of the valley [4370 2015] 4 m of sandstone were seen in beds up to 0.25 m thick separated by thin partings of silty shale.

A cutting [4643 2200] on the west side of the A386 Torrington–Bideford road reveals 1 m of horizontal massive brownish grey sandstone with bottom-structures, on 0.5 m of grey silty shales with sandstone beds up to 100 mm thick, on 0.25 m of fine-grained sandstone. Some 200 m to the SE [4659 2187] 2 m of rather nodular grey silty shaly mudstone occupy the hinge-region of a northerly-overturned anticline. At 100 m farther ESE 5 m of thickly bedded sandstones rest on 3.1 m of grey silty shales with thin sandstone beds; the dip is 40°/155°.

On the west side of the A386 road 250 m W of Beam Mansion, a cutting [4701 2074] reveals the following sequence:

	Thickness m
Sandstone, massive, flute-casts on base	1.0
Shales, dark grey, cleaved and contorted	5.1
Sandstone, massive	0.8
Shales, dark grey contorted	0 to 0.1
Sandstones in beds up to 0.5 m thick, with shaly partings	2.0
Shales, grey silty, largely overgrown	5.5
Mudstones, grey silty, with sandstone beds up to 50 mm thick	5.1

A northward-overturned anticline and complementary syncline are exposed in a quarry [4722 2099] 300 m N of Beam Mansion. The sequence is massive sandstone 1.55 m, overlain by grey silty shales with sandstone beds up to 50 mm thick 1.45 m and thinly bedded sandstones 1.35 m.

At 350 m SW of Beam Mansion is the large Beam Quarry [471 204] of the Braunton Sand Company. The sequence exposed in 1972, in an asymmetric anticline, was as follows:

	Thickness m
Sandstones, thickly bedded	2.10
Sandstones, medium-bedded with shale partings up to 100 mm thick	3.10
Shales, dark grey silty	1.45
Sandstones, medium-bedded, with flute-casts and grey silty shale partings	2.95
Mudstones, grey silty with sandstone beds up to 30 mm thick	2.95
Mudstones, grey silty with sandstone beds up to 0.3 m thick	2.55
Mudstones, dark grey silty, with sandstone beds up to 50 mm thick	1.45
Sandstone, hard very fine-grained	1.20
Mudstones, dark grey shaly silty	1.25
Sandstone, hard fine-grained muddy	3.45
Siltstones, banded pale and dark grey, cleaved	0.30
Sandstone, hard fine-grained	1.15
Mudstones, grey and dark grey, finely banded, cleaved	1.00
Mudstones, dark grey silty	2.90

West Putford to Melbury

The high moorland around Melbury and Common Moor bears a thick mantle (up to 5 m) of heavy yellowish brown clay with scattered sandstone fragments. Rare exposures of massive sandstones occur in the valley of the River Torridge east of West Putford, and in the smaller stream sections. Thus 0.5 m of pale and dark grey banded siltstones overlie 2.1 m of massive sandstone on

1.25 m of grey shaly mudstones, dipping 50°/185°, in a stream bed [3731 1524] near Bountis Thorne, and sporadic exposures of sandstone in beds up to 0.5 m thick occur in a stream section 1.5 km to the NE, between [3825 1650] and [3825 1638].

Tythecott–Langtree–Torrington

Sporadic exposures of thickly bedded and massive sandstones occur in the bed of the Lydeland Water and its tributaries; a particularly massive sandstone 1.95 m thick crops out at [4091 1906], vertically disposed. Farther east, in a disused quarry [4293 1774] at Hembury Castle, 3.55 m of sandstone in beds up to 0.25 m thick with thin silty shale partings dip 30°/150°. There are several disused quarries on Langtree Common. In a quarry [4606 1574] 500 m SE of Buda, 10 m of sandstone in beds up to 0.75 m thick with thin shaly partings dip 55°/185°, and 200 m to the NE, in another disused quarry [4620 1584], medium- and thinly bedded brown-weathered sandstones with brownish grey sandy mudstone partings dip 85°/170°. Some 200 m to the N, on the west bank of the Langtree Lake stream, are two large disused quarries [462 160]. They show a periclinal fold plunging 10°/280° in about 15 m of thickly bedded and massive sandstones with a variety of bottom-structures.

At Watergate Bridge, a small occasionally-worked quarry [4695 1765] contains a sequence of hard massive brownish grey sandstone, in beds up to 0.5 m thick, with bedding-plane slicken-sides. At Taddiport, in a roadside cutting [4850 1845], 7 m of brownish grey fine-grained sandstone in beds up to 0.5 m thick separated by thin shaly partings dip 45°/190°. Farther south, near Bagbear, a small occasionally-worked quarry contains the following sequence:

	Thickness m
Sandstone, medium-bedded	2.1
Mudstones, dark grey shaly, with siltstone beds up to 0.1 m thick and sandstone beds up to 0.15 m thick	2.0
Sandstone, greenish grey hard fine-grained, in beds up to 0.3 m thick	5.0

Abbots Bickington to Bulkworthy

Exposures hereabouts are mostly confined to the valley of the River Torridge. Sporadic outcrops of thickly bedded and massive sandstones with flute-casts and load-casts occur for 200 m upstream of Haytown Bridge [3830 1425].

Newton St Petrock to Peters Marland

Sporadic exposures, usually of thickly bedded sandstones, occur in the valley of the River Torridge and its tributaries. About 10 m of medium- and thickly bedded sandstones crop out in a stream section [4068 1272 to 4071 1280] near Newton St Petrock. Farther east, in the valley of the Mussel Brook, 2 m of sandstone in beds up to 0.2 m thick with thin sandy mudstone partings dip 40°/290° [4613 1190]. In a small disused quarry [4898 1196] near the eastern margin of the district 3 m of sandstone dip 30° N. The sandstone is mainly thickly bedded, but very thinly bedded in places; the thick sandstones bear load-casts 80 to 100 mm across.   BJW

Lana to Cookbury Moor

Fine-grained sandstones have been quarried from several small pits between Lana [3005 0730] and Rhude [3095 0700]. In the westernmost [3006 0638] the strata are fairly thickly bedded and silty and dip 60°/005°. In another [3067 0693] the rock is blocky and locally feldspathic and appears to dip 65°/355°.

Chilsworthy is a linear village which spans three sandstone ridges trending just N of E. Sandstone rubble abounds and there are traces of old diggings [3246 0657; 3265 0686]. Slightly nodular shales and silty shales of the lower ground between the ridges dip 25°/345° in one place [3284 0631] and are prominent in the Head at another [3270 0656].

Valleyside pits near Babington show massive and thickly bedded fine-grained sandstone with partings of silty micaceous shale and silty sandstone, in the core of an anticline (p.45) [3378 0694], and blocky fine-grained feldspathic sandstone [3387 0690]. A little over 0.5 km to the S, near North Hogspark, horizontal strata alongside an old canal embankment [3376 0633] comprise fine-grained sandstone in beds up to 0.4 m thick with interbedded silty sandstone and silty shale containing plant debris. Excavations at nearby Thorne Park revealed fine- to medium-grained blocky feldspathic sandstone with some mica [3433 0618]. Argillaceous beds of the lower ground hereabouts are exposed near the old canal [3415 0591] as black laminated siltstones with scattered thin sandstones and micaceous carbonaceous sandy shales, dipping 35°/310° and gently northwards.

Three disused, filled or flooded sandstone quarries [3677 0577; 3688 0581; 3731 0581] lie between Blagdonmoor Wharf and Halsdon Barton. Another, to the north [3842 0658], in a small island of 'solid' rising above a terrace flat, shows thickly bedded fine- and medium-grained feldspathic sandstone with some thinly bedded silty sandstone containing plant fragments. The strata are vertical, striking E–W, and carry finely crystalline quartz on N–S joint faces. Grey silty mudstone adjoins the sandstone in the south wall of the quarry.

Fine-grained thinly bedded sandstones with interbedded shales strike around E–W in a stream [3776 0737 to 3780 0732] 1.5 km E of Brendon; they are vertical or northward dipping.

Cookbury to Highweek

Fine-grained, locally micaceous sandstones strike E–W around Little Lashbrook [406 071], and some blocks of sugary feldspathic sandstone were found on S-facing valley slopes south-west of the farm. Similar rocks near the base of the formation in and near Cookbury [4098 0591; 4103 0604] are in places [4081 0600] interbedded with siltstone and carry silty nodules up to 50 mm across. An old pit [4126 0682] 1 km NNE of the village shows fine-grained thickly bedded brown and grey sandstones with mica and plant fragments.

The basal sandstone group of the Bude Formation forms a ridge extending from Highpark to Highweek. A quarry [4165 0540] near the former exposes fine-grained grey quartz-sandstone weathering to brown, with a gentle northerly dip. Similarly-dipping buff micaceous sandstone crops out at Highweek [4459 0569] and sugary micaceous sandstone rubble lies scattered north of the farm. The area to the north, bounded by the ridge, Bradford [4210 0725] and the River Torridge, contains a number of scattered outcrops, mainly of fine-grained sandstone with mica and plant fragments. A NE-flowing tributary stream of the Torridge cuts through much thinly bedded and thickly bedded sandstone, shale and silty shale showing both northerly and southerly dips [4234 0579 to 4305 0647]. In Highweek Wood silty shales dip 60° S [4443 0622] and fine-grained thickly bedded sandstones dip at 45° or more northwards [4449 0626; 4461 0627]. Old quarries near the confluence of the Whiteleigh Water and the River Torridge show fine-grained buff, green, and purple sandstones with layers of plant debris [4392 0640], and fine-grained purplish buff sandstones with silty shales [4394 0635]; dips are generally around 80° northerly, but gentler at the top of the first-mentioned quarry.

On the north side of the River Torridge hereabouts thickly bedded fine-grained sandstones have been dug [4498 0644] southeast of West Libbear, and massive and thickly bedded fine-grained micaceous sandstones [4483 0736; 4497 0740] east-north-east of Worden. Silty micaceous shales [4499 0738] adjoining the latter sandstones dip 75°/355°.

Libbear Barton to Sheepwash

Fine-grained hard micaceous sandstones, generally thinly bedded with some shales, crop out in the stream course [4522 0712 to 4530 0706] north of Libbear Barton. Dips are northerly, both gentle and steep, but locally [4527 0708] the beds are vertical, striking 350° adjacent to a fault. A S-flowing stream passing between Wooda and South Hill has exposed much fine-grained sandstone with some shales [4650 0746 to 4634 0664], generally striking between ENE and ESE and vertical or dipping northwards at between 5° and 85°. An old pit [4644 0739] shows near-horizontal thickly bedded fine-grained brown sandstone 1 m, overlain by silty shale and silt-stone with some silty nodules 1.5 m, and rubbly sandstone 0.6 m. A short distance downstream massive and thickly bedded fine-grained and micaceous sandstones [4641 0728] adjoin thickly bedded sandstones with load-casts [4640 0726]; the dip is 85°–90°N. Massive sandstones are locally associated with siltstones and silty shales [4630 0704].

The basal strata of the formation are well exposed along the south side of the River Torridge in the neighbourhood of Coham and Black Torrington. Massive sandstones of the bottom group have been quarried [4537 0583] in the small valley west of Coham, and bedded sandstones crop out in a lane [4565 0600] at the farm. Thickly bedded greenish grey and buff sandstones trending N of E through the northern outskirts of Black Torrington [4636 0570; 4672 0585] are locally associated with siltstones and shales [4666 0578; 467 058]. Small quarries alongside the north-flowing stream east of the village show thickly bedded sandstones dipping 45°–50°NNW [4690 0586; 4691 0591; 4694 0593]. In one place [4689 0595] massive and thickly bedded brown sandstones contain siltstone partings dipping 5°/280°, probably adjacent to a N–S fault, and are shown by the position of load-casts to be right way up.

Thickly bedded and massive basal sandstones, locally displaced by faults, crop out farther east [4719 0603; 4748 0600; 4752 0606]. Quarries in the bottom sandstone group near Herrick's Mill show greyish buff sandstones [4832 0572; 4852 0571] with shales [4841 0571; 4862 0572] dipping 40°–60°/350°–005°.

Northward of these basal beds massive sandstones crop out in the farmyard at South Gortleigh [4666 0643] and thickly bedded sandstones have been dug farther east [4779 0676; 4793 0653]. Sandstones in an old pit [4879 0724] 1 km N of Sheepwash show reddening and probably lie close to a NW–SE fault.

Dunsdon to Barrow

A small disused quarry [3012 0837] near Dunsdon shows a 3.5-m face of massive fine-grained sandstone. A small E–W valley to the north is cut along the strike of shales with silty shales and silty sandstones [3018 0891 to 3030 0891] dipping north or slightly west of north. Wooda Farm [3045 0922] stands on another broad sandstone ridge, to the north of which a second E–W valley runs in shales and silty shales with a little siltstone and thinly bedded silty sandstone [3021 0960 to 3091 0957]. The beds are fissile and generally dip 30°–70°/345°–015° although locally they are nearly vertical. Fine-grained sandstones of the ridge to the north are exposed [3011 0974] alongside the old Bude Canal, near to over-lying silty shales and shaly siltstones with some silty sandstones and silty nodules [3012 0977] dipping 35°/010°.

A similar sequence of fine-grained thinly and thickly bedded sandstones dipping north or east of north beneath shales with thin sandstones occurs in a stream course [3097 0902 to 3100 0912] 1 km to the SE. Some 8 m of the sandstones are exposed [3119 0885] near

West Hamsworthy, fine-grained in beds up to 0.5 m thick with interbedded shales up to 0.3 m and dipping 30°N. Shales, mud-stones and siltstones with thin sandstones dip 45°/360° [3119 0831] and 75°/170° [3120 0827] near Slade and are exposed farther east in a stream [3178 0857 to 3204 0884] running south-westwards just west of West Youldon. This section shows mudstones and micaceous siltstones at the southern end, thinly bedded fine-grained sandstones with interbedded shales and siltstones in the central part [3178 0858 to 3186 0870], and shales and silty shales farther north-east. Dips are all northerly in the range 10°–80°/345°–005°.

An old pit [3260 0994] just east of Lufflands shows fine-grained thinly bedded sandstones in the south wall dipping 25°/340°, and silty sandstones and siltstones with some stronger more massive fine-grained sandstone in the north wall, inclined 15°/350°. Sand-stones, shales and siltstones are sporadically exposed in stream courses [3326 0804 to 3349 0913] near Greyland and Honeycroft; northerly dips of 25°–50° are typical except towards the southern-most point where some shales with thin sandstones dip gently southwards, and fine-grained sandstones northwards.

An old quarry [3324 0756] east of Ugworthy has recently been worked again. Fine-grained thinly bedded sandstones, locally thicker bedded and strong and in places accompanied by shales, pass northwards from vertical, strike 100°, to dips of 45°/180° and vertical, strike 100°. Several other small disused pits lie scattered within the area to the north and east [3364 0994; 3353 0962; 3383 0909; 3458 0912; 3468 0765].

In the stream course east and north-east of East Vognacott thinly bedded fine-grained hard grey sandstone with some shaly partings [3409 0759] dips 85°N beneath shales and siltstones with silty sandstones [3410 0761]; and thinly bedded fine-grained sandstones [3416 0770] dip 75°/005° beneath shales, silty shales, micaceous siltstones and silty sandstones [3419 0773]. Some 300 m to the NE the ENE-trending valley is seen to be cut in argillaceous strata comprising shales, silty shales, micaceous siltstones and silty sandstones [3439 0794 to 3448 0796] dipping 20°–60°/340°–355°.

Holsworthy Beacon to Thornbury

The valley trending ENE near Langadon, 1.5 km N of Holsworthy Beacon, is cut roughly along the strike of grey and black shales, silty shales, silty mudstones and locally micaceous siltstones with some thin fine-grained sandstones [3566 0976 to 3590 0983; 3582 0987]. Dips around 20°/330°–350° are common. The sand-stone ridge to the south, on which East Paddon stands, contains two small old sandstone pits [3619 0963; 3636 0990] and one larger one [3622 0974]. This last shows, at its western end, 10 m of thickly bedded and massive fine-grained sandstones with shaly partings and much plant debris dipping 10°/350°. Some 3 m of similar strata at the eastern end dip 15°/350°. Fairly thickly bedded sandstones to the south [3622 0965] are traversed by quartz veinlets.

A ridge extending from Forda to Woodacott Cross has been pitted locally for sandstone, as near the former locality where rubbly thickly bedded fine-grained feldspathic sandstone is ex-posed [3780 0759]. A trench [3813 0770] near Woodacott passed southwards from sandstone into shale.

Exposures at Down [3712 0878] show a similar relationship, with fine-grained sandstones of the ridge overlying the shales which occupy the slight depression to the south. The ridge is cut by a stream to the west of the farm, where fairly thickly bedded fine-grained sandstones dip 5°/010° [3664 0884]. These sandstones pass beneath argillaceous strata occupying the steep-sided valley to the north, wherein grey and black shales with thinly bedded papery fine-grained sandstones [3672 0905 to 3685 0921] dip 65°–80°N. Both West Wonford [3700 0965] and East Wonford [3795 0960] stand on higher ground to the north littered with much sandstone debris.

Stream sections near Berry [3865 0945], Thorne [3885 0865] and Bagbeare [3940 0925] show shales, siltstones and fine-grained sandstones dipping 45°–70°/345°–360° [3903 0943; 3903 0933] and 15°/170° [3899 0916]. Traces of old pits are common hereabouts.

An old quarry [3945 0761] 1 km SW of Thornbury contains many blocks of fine-grained sandstone. In and alongside a stream just north-west of the village shales with siltstones and thin fine-grained sandstones dip 20°–90°/355°–015° and show silty nodules [3967 0877] and small-scale folding [3975 0878].

Thornbury to Shebbear

About 1.5 km N of Thornbury an old quarry on the slopes of the River Waldon valley shows the section illustrated in Figure 4. The dip is generally about 10°/350°, but the basal sandstones show indications of the SSE-dipping southern limb of a gentle anticline.

Sporadic exposures occur downstream along this valley to the south-south-east. Near Thornbury Mill fine-grained buff feldspathic micaceous sandstones with some silty and shaly beds [4019 0914] dip 55°/360° beneath shaly siltstones and silty shales [4019 0916]. Near to an old quarry [4060 0933] on the eastern slopes of the valley 5 m of thickly bedded fine-grained grey sandstones [4056 9028] are sandwiched between shales with thinly bedded sandstones dipping 45°/005°. Southwards from here, small exposures are common on the steep valley slopes.

An old pit [4074 0775] 1 km SE of Thornbury contains 2 m of fairly thinly bedded fine-grained grey sandstone dipping 12°/350°, and exposures [4134 0785] at Bason Cross show shales dipping 60°/360° beneath sandstones. At 170 m to the E a densely overgrown pit [4150 0785] contains much rubbly fine-grained greenish grey sandstone, some of it feldspathic and micaceous, together with grey platy siltstone.

Many small exposures occur on the steep slopes of the Torridge valley north of its junction with the River Waldon, especially on Gidcott Clapper Hills [422 091] and in Castle Wood [426 086]. At 550 m NE of Henscott thickly bedded fine-grained sandstones, locally with feldspar and mica, appear to dip 45°/350° [4224 0907]. On the opposite (eastern) banks [4260 0919] massive and thickly bedded grey feldspathic sandstone with plant fragments 1.2 m, is overlain by shales with thinly bedded sandstones 1.4 m, and fine-grained rubbly sandstone 1.3 m; the beds dip 45°/005°.

An old quarry [4368 0950] at Pitt, Shebbear, shows, in the north face, massive and thickly bedded fine-grained grey feldspathic sandstone 7 m, overlain by thinly bedded sandstones and shaly beds 5 m; the dip is 30°/360°. In the east face similar strata are disposed in an anticline whose limbs dip 30°/360° and 25°/130°. The folded and fractured rocks of the west face are shown in Figure 5; the fractures are strike faults trending E–W to pass just south of the exposed east face.

East of the village fine-grained buff sugary sandstone is exposed [4455 0981] near Shebbear College; a disused sandstone quarry [4478 0863] near New Inn has been filled and fine-grained thinly bedded feldspathic and micaceous sandstone with plant fragments dips 45°/010° at Hill [4485 0783].

Battledown Cross to Filleigh Moor

The stream flowing SSE from just east of Battledown Cross contains sporadic exposures, mainly of fine-grained sandstone [4544 0920 to 4647 0765], and a few disused small sandstone quarries occur on the valley slopes [4548 0920; 4583 0774; 4653 0798]. One such exposure [4611 0800] shows fine- and fine- to medium-grained, greyish green and buff, micaceous sandstones in beds up to 1 m thick with interbedded micaceous siltstones and silty shales, locally rich in plant fragments. Slickensiding indicates some slip on bedding planes. Some 4 m of strata are exposed, and they dip 15°/010°.

E-trending sandstone ridges extend to the SSE-flowing Mussel Brook. The beds between the ridges were seen in Buckland Wood [4686 0866] to comprise micaceous siltstones showing nodular weathering, and in Upcott Wood [4724 0821] to be interbedded shales, micaceous siltstones and silty sandstones.

The main outcrops along the valley of the Mussel Brook are as follows: at [4739 0986] fine- to medium-grained thickly bedded greyish green micaceous sandstones enclosing ovoids of weathered friable micaceous medium-grained sandstone, dip 20°/160°; at [4732 0897] thickly bedded fine-grained sandstones with plant fragments and with partings of platy sandstone, dip 15°/360°; at [4748 0888] an overgrown quarry in buff thickly bedded fine-grained sandstones; at [4786 0816] 4 m of greenish grey micaceous fine-grained sandstones in beds up to 0.3 m thick, with interbedded shales, horizontal or with a slight northerly dip.

An overgrown roadside quarry [4866 0998] west of Netherton contains argillaceous sandstones with shales and siltstones, and shales and siltstones immediately to the south [4866 0994] dip 65°/360°.

The stream running south-east from Filleigh Moor cuts through many small outcrops of shales, siltstones, mudstones and fine-grained flaggy sandstones [4885 0836 to 4945 0797].

Virworthy and Soldon Cross to Sutcombe

The E–W ridge on which Virworthy [3126 1033] stands has been quarried about 1 km W of the farm; no outcrop remains but the banks of the small flooded pit [3026 1028] contain fragments of fine-grained sandstone. Exposures near the farm include siltstones, shales and silty sandstones in the roadside [3135 1041], silty sandstones, siltstones and shales striking E–W in a stream course [3137 1039] and dipping at moderate angles to north and south, and fine-grained sandstone in an old pit [3141 1042].

The ridge is separated from a similar and parallel rise to the north by a depression in which silty shales and mudstones crop out [3006 1042], dipping around 10° NNW. This second ridge also has been pitted [3010 1084] but no exposures remain. A valley to the north shows vertical black shales striking E–W [3096 1115] and is succeeded farther north by another ridge, bearing traces of pits and scattered debris of fine-grained sandstone, a depression without exposures, and a broad ridge upon which stand South Newland [3060 1206] and North Newland [3071 1215]. This last ridge contains remains of a slightly larger quarry [3031 1208] in fine-grained sandstones with shales, and two others [3029 1190; 3104 1212] which contain debris of fine-grained sandstone but no outcrops.

Soldon Cottage [3235 1030] stands on the divide between two valley heads. To the west a stream runs slightly south of west to Virworthy Mill and contains scattered exposures of thin platy siltstones, silty sandstones, silty shales and mudstones; the beds strike along the valley with local deviations of up to 10° or so, and dip at 45°–75° northerly or are vertical. To the east of Soldon Cottage, Lovers Lake runs east-north-east between a well-defined ridge to the south, on which stands Hole [3370 1027] and in which an old quarry [3304 1013] shows 2 m of fine-grained platy sandstones with some siltstones overlain by 1 m of silty shales dipping 10°/015°, and a broad ridge to the north on which stands Soldon Manor [3276 1080]. An exposure [3355 1058] in Lovers Lake shows shales, silty shales and siltstones dipping north. Soldon Manor ridge trends ENE and E and bears blocks of fine-grained sandstone scattered throughout brown silty soil. A small disused quarry [3296 1115] has been used as a tip, but the rubble of fine-grained greyish green argillaceous sandstone and slightly coarser brown sandstone probably reflects the underlying rock.

A narrow ENE-trending valley to the north contains grey and black silty shales and siltstones with thin fine-grained sandstones striking E–W, vertical or dipping steeply north [3283 1122; 3286

1123]. Farther north towards Instaple [3234 1200] several poorly defined ridges trend E or slightly N of E. Foundation trenches for a silo at the farm showed fine-grained greyish green and brown sandstone. Alongside a lane to the east [3273 1195] shales, mudstones, siltstones and fine-grained sandstones dip at 25° and 70° to N or just E of N.

The River Waldon west and south of Sutcombe meanders in a broad flood plain and contains no exposures, except for 5 m of grey silty shales which dip 85°/340° [3349 1159] at the eastern edge of the alluvial flat.

Mudstones, siltstones and fine-grained sandstones crop out in the roadside [3500 1034] near Thuborough Barton. A stream to the north-west had been recently dug out at the time of survey and showed continuous exposure for 270 m [3450 1045 to 3073 1059]. The rocks comprised shales, mudstones and siltstones with some finely banded silty sandstones. Strikes were everywhere around E–W, but dips were unreliable owing to the rubbly nature of the exposures.

A well-defined E–W ridge between these argillaceous rocks and the River Waldon at Sutcombemill contains several exposures. A quarry [3476 1068] on the south side has been cut in 9 m of massive and thickly bedded fine-grained greyish green sandstones dipping 30°S. A quarry [3462 1089] on the north side shows 8 m of thickly bedded fine-grained greyish green and brown sandstones, locally thinner bedded towards the top.

The river at Sutcombemill probably follows a band of argillaceous rocks, on the north side of which 6 m of shales and silty shales with a little thinly bedded sandstone [3483 1118] dip 60°–70° S, and are succeeded to the north by fine-grained sandstones. A nearby exposure [3471 1118] shows 15 m of strata, mainly thickly bedded fine-grained sandstones but with shale bands up to 2.5 m thick, vertical and striking roughly E–W.

Rubble in Sutcombe cemetery [3466 1150] is mainly of shale with some fine-grained sandstone, but the village itself stands on a rise mainly underlain by sandstone. Fine-grained sandstones [3482 1172] form a floor to the lane leading down to a stream to the east. An old quarry [3487 1168] alongside the stream shows massive and thinner bedded fine-grained sandstones with shaly partings. Laneside exposures east of the stream show fine-grained sandstones with shaly and silty partings, vertical and trending 085°, amid a good deal of shaly spoil [3494 1181]; also fine-grained sandstones in beds up to 0.3 m thick and dipping 70° N with some interbedded shales, silty shales and siltstones [3496 1180].

Old pits in the valley east of Sutcombe rectory show rubbly fine-grained sandstones with silty shales containing plant fragments [3456 1228], and fine-grained sandstones with shaly partings, vertical and striking approximately E–W [3461 1232].

Bradworthy area

Kimworthy [3110 1275] stands on a rise bearing scattered sandstone fragments in brown silty soil. In a small valley to the north shales and silty mudstones with a little sandstone are vertical and strike E–W [3170 1322], and fine-grained sandstones dip 85°/010° [3140 1334]. Streamside exposures [3130 1405] farther north show thinly bedded sandstones and shales dipping 45° N, and at Berridon [3121 1457], blocky greyish green fine-grained sandstone is cut by a small E–W fault.

A number of exposures occur alongside the River Waldon west of Bradworthy. Just south of the road to Worden, old pits [3183 1395; 3186 1391] contain rubble of greyish green fine-grained bedded sandstone. At Bradworthy Mill [3193 1406] shales with a little fine-grained sandstone and siltstone dip 75°/350°. On the west bank of the river farther north a quarry [3180 1435] currently not in use but owned by E.C.C. Quarries Ltd contains the following beds disposed in an anticline (pp. 45–46, Figure 10):

	Thickness m
Fine-grained sandstones, locally in beds up to 2 m thick, in places thinner bedded with traces of load-casts; and with shaly partings up to 0.3 m thick showing axial-plane cleavage	16.0
Shales with thin silty sandstones	0.7
Fine-grained thickly bedded sandstones	2.5
Shales with thin silty sandstones	0.5
Fine-grained thickly bedded sandstones	1.6

A quarry [3191 1435] on the opposite, eastern, side of the stream shows steeply inclined or vertical fine-grained thickly bedded sandstones with thin shale bands, resembling the higher beds of the western quarry. Load-casts are visible high in the south-east corner of the quarry. The beds strike E–W.

Farther upstream to the north fine-grained sandstones crop out sporadically. Near Spittle [3155 1486] they contain a belt of grey shales showing gentle north-north-westerly [3152 1489] and steeper south-south-easterly [3179 1485] dips and cleavage inclined north-north-west [3177 1496].

A few rubbly outcrops of fine-grained sandstone, locally thinly bedded and platy with a little shale, occur in Bradworthy. The N–S valley to the east, comprising the southerly flowing stretch of the River Waldon near Waterland Mill [3295 1306] and the tributary stream joining it from Lake Villa [3300 1447], contains several small disused quarries. The southernmost [3306 1277] has been used as a dump but yields fragments of fine-grained sandstone. Another pit [3305 1294], west of Northcott, shows hard compact brown fine-grained sandstone, fairly massive in the main (eastern) face but bedded and with prominent load-casts in the southern face; the strata are vertical, striking E–W and younging south. Old quarries nearer Lake Villa show fragments of fine-grained sandstone [3294 1417], brown and greenish grey fine-grained sandstones dipping 45°/350° [3289 1426], and less well exposed similar fine-grained sandstones [3298 1431; 3292 1440; 3292 1443; 3318 1470; 3318 1474].

Fine-grained platy sandstones are exposed [3354 1357] in the roadside just west of Cleverdon House. A small quarry [3375 1419] 550 m to the N is now largely grassed, with fragments of brown fine-grained sandstone. Farther east a stream system flowing southwards from near Silworthy [3426 1459] shows rubbly outcrops of fine-grained sandstones [3438 1294; 3444 1351; 3427 1384] with a little shale [3442 1336]. The sandstones have been dug from small pits [3451 1340; 3452 1346; 3478 1395] for local use.

Upcott to Milton Damerel and Woodford Bridge

Shales dip 65°/175° in a lane [3579 1048] near Thuborough Mill and siltstones and silty shales strike slightly north of east in a stream [3575 1017] to the south. Fine-grained sandstones have been worked in a nearby quarry [3620 1037] but the River Waldon, from Thuborough Mill to Miltonmill Bridge [3772 1029], probably runs over predominantly argillaceous strata.

Upcott [3515 1137], Hawkwill [3585 1139] and Matcott [3593 1158] stand on a sandstone rise, but shales, silty shales and mudstones crop out south [3530 1112; 3530 1133; 3535 1135] and north [3521 1153] of the first two farms, striking approximately E–W and dipping at moderate or steep angles to north and south. In the N–S stream valley to the east thickly bedded and massive fine-grained sandstones have been quarried [3649 1081; 3658 1081] just upstream of the confluence with the River Waldon.

Traces of old diggings [3643 1125] in sandstone farther upstream lie between two belts of argillaceous strata trending slightly N of E. Silty shales in the southern belt [3633 1115 to 3633 1117] dip 45°–60° N; a roadside outcrop [3653 1138] on the north side of the northern belt shows 5 m of shales and silty shales dipping 45°–

60°/353° beneath 1 m of rubbly sandstone. The ENE-trending stream south of Youldon shows scattered outcrops [3635 1214 to 3683 1233] of shales, silty shales and siltstones with thinly bedded sandstones; the strike is around E–W and the dip vertical or steep northerly. Fine-grained sandstone has been dug [3608 1242; 3613 1257] west of Youldon.

An old quarry [3720 1192] east of Great Derworthy shows fairly massive fine-grained grey-green and brown sandstones with a few thin quartz veins, a little red staining and traces of nearly horizontal fractures.

Roadside outcrops around Venn Green and Venn show silty shales, mudstones and siltstones with some thinly bedded silty sandstone to the south and north of an ill-defined sandstone ridge. The southerly exposures display dips of 85°S [3750 1106] and 45°N [3800 1112]; the northerly exposure 70°N [3788 1131].

An old quarry [3768 1019] south-west of Milton Mill is cut in fine-grained sandstone. Exposures in Milton Mill show 5 m of thickly bedded fine-grained sandstones with a few shaly partings dipping 10°/345° [3782 1031], and successively northwards similar sandstones [3783 1033] and shales [3783 1036].

Milton Damerel stands on a broad rise underlain by fine-grained sandstones, in which grassed pits [3850 1080; 3851 1083] lie north-north-east of Holy Trinity Church. Silty shales and siltstones to the south dip 85°N [3858 1045] to pass beneath the sandstones.

A disused roadside quarry [3918 1021] west-south-west of Gratton shows 4.5 m of fine-grained thickly bedded sandstones overlain by 2.5 m of silty shales, siltstones and thin silty sandstones. In places the shales carry rust spots after pyrite, and the beds dip 10°/285°. A nearly vertical small fault trends just N of E through the section.

The valley of the Fishpool Lake contains silty shales with hard thin siltstones, some silty sandstones and scattered sandy nodules of the same shaly beds that crop out south of Venn Green and Venn. They dip 30°–45° southerly [3865 1107; 3864 1109]. The same argillaceous strata trend ENE thence and crop out as rubbly roadside exposures. Between Whitebear [3929 1123] and Park House [3931 1143] they are seen to comprise shales, silty shales, siltstones and thin silty sandstones dipping between north and north-north-west at 20°–80°.

Farther upstream alongside the Fishpool Lake hard greyish green fine-grained sandstones have been worked in a quarry [3860 1141]. The beds appear to dip steeply northwards, and brecciated sandstone and quartz veins suggest the presence of faulting.

Horrellsford lies in a small ENE-trending valley cut in mainly argillaceous rocks. An old quarry [3848 1164] contains sandstone fragments but exposures of black shales. Finely banded sandstones, silty sandstones and silty shales [3854 1163] appear to dip westwards, possibly as a result of faulting or valleyward creep. By the roadside to the east [3869 1162; 3874 1162] shales and fine-grained sandstones dip steeply just west of north.

A small steep-sided valley trends ENE towards Woodford Bridge. Silty shales are exposed high on the northern flanks [3941 1243], and in the valley bottom silty shales with some shales and siltstones dip 60°/175° [3966 1240].   EAE

CHAPTER 3
Permian and Eocene

PERMIAN

A small outlier of presumed Permian rocks occurs on the coast near Portledge and Peppercombe, and extends about 2 km inland to the east. Permian rocks are faulted against Bude Formation strata at the northern margin of the outlier, and rest unconformably upon them at the western coastal boundary. The rocks are breccias with beds of sand and sandstone and scattered calcareous bands and nodules. There is no direct evidence of their age but they generally resemble the Permian breccias of south and central Devon. The rocks of this outlier have been described in detail in the Geological Survey memoir relating to the Bideford district (Edmonds, Williams and Taylor, 1979).

EOCENE

The Orleigh Court flint-gravel outlier covers an area approximately 800 m by 800 m, about 1 km NE of Buckland Brewer. A general account of these rocks has been given by Edmonds, Williams and Taylor (1979).

A road cutting [4272 2263] 400 m NW of Orleigh Court shows 1 m of reddish brown to buff sand with scattered poorly rounded nodular flints. Sporadic exposures [429 223] at The Rookery are of fine- to coarse-grained sand containing brownish grey nodular subrounded flints of various sizes, with a few yellowish brown and black flints. In places the flints are abundant and the matrix sparse.   BJW

CHAPTER 4

Structure

GENERAL ACCOUNT

The Upper Carboniferous rocks of the Bude district lie within a major synclinorial structure formed during the Variscan orogeny. The axis of this fold crosses the coast near Duckpool [200 115] and trends generally eastwards to pass north of Buckland Filleigh [470 093] and on into the Chulmleigh (309) district (Figure 7). Other lesser east–west-trending anticlinoria and synclinoria occur farther north; the anticlinorium passing through Embury [216 961] brings up Crackington Formation from beneath its cover of Bude Formation, and the complementary synclinorium to the north through Longpeak [220 230] is in Bude Formation.

The folding probably occurred at a very late stage in the orogeny. Compressive forces which may have begun in late Devonian times farther south caused thrusting and over-folding south of the district and also possibly to the north along the line of the conjectural Exmoor Thrust. Folds of the Bude district originated within the central part of the fold belt and at a high tectonic level. Compression caused crumpling, arching up of the district and consequent cessation of sedimentation. Some gravity sliding with resultant disruption of earlier relatively upright folds appears to have followed. The relatively thin Upper Carboniferous rocks probably formed a crumpled sheet separated from the highly deformed rocks below by a décollement plane which possibly reaches the surface as the Rusey Thrust near Boscastle (Freshney, McKeown and Williams, 1972). Cleavage is not well developed; it occurs as a fracture cleavage in the noses of the folds, particularly those with the more acute interlimb angles.

Relaxation of the pressure during the Permian allowed the development of east–west normal faults, horsts and grabens. The north-west to south-east faults, and other associated transcurrent faults, were probably initiated during the main compressive movements. Immediately to the east such faults are known to have been active during Eocene and Oligocene times (Freshney, Beer and Wright, 1979) and some movement probably occurs even now.

FOLDS

Impressed upon most of the major warps are swarms of periclinal planar-limbed folds trending between east and east-north-east. These periclines range in length from a few tens of metres to several hundreds of metres, with limb lengths up to about 500 m. The interlimb angles range from 40° to 150° but most are around 80°–90°. There is some tendency for the more southerly folds to have more acute interlimb angles. Variation in these angles has been discussed by Sanderson (1974), who attributed the southerly change to an increase in strain in this direction; this accords with other structural features, such as a southerly increase in the intensity of cleavage and the amount of thrusting.

The sense of overturning of the folds is highly variable and appears to be related to position both on the flanks of the major anticlinoria and synclinoria and within the structural belt as a whole. From south of Bude northwards to northing [079] the folds are overturned to the south or near-vertical, while from around Northcott Mouth to the major synclinorial axis at Duckpool the folds range from upright to overturned to the north. North of Duckpool, however, the folds are strongly overturned to the south, and this is particularly true of the larger folds; thus the anticline whose axis runs just north of Stanbury Mouth has an axial plane which dips 35°N. North of this last flexure near-upright folds with limbs of roughly equal lengths bring about much repetition of strata. Relatively upright folds (Plate 7) persist to Welcombe Mouth, beyond which northerly overturning is common; the major fold at Embury is quite strongly over-turned to the north. The apparent control by major folds of the direction of overturning in minor folds suggests that either the lesser folds predate the greater, or that they were contemporaneous, generated at a higher level in the crust, and 'flowed' down the flanks of the major fold to produce opposing senses of overturning on opposite flanks.

Somewhat incongruous sets of recumbent folds, box folds and crumples are developed at different places in the coastal section (Plate 1). Many of these anomalous folds, especially the box folds and crumples on the steep limbs of major folds, have no preferred facing orientation. Commonly, however, the recumbent folds, which usually occur towards the apexes of upright folds, show definite preferred orientations over certain parts of the section. In the south of the district they face both north and south, but from Sandy Mouth to about 1 km N of Duckpool the facing direction is consistently towards the north. Farther north, facing directions are once more variable. From Stanbury Mouth to Knaps Longpeak these folds face consistently southwards; farther north they face to the north. Probably all these anomalous folds were generated at a high level in the tectonic pile, and they may be gravity structures. The box folds and the non-directional crumples could have developed as a response to static load with low side-confining pressure, but the recumbent folds showing variable facing directions suggest that some lateral translation was taking place, probably by gravity sliding.

Facing directions of the recumbent folds generally indicate a sense of movement towards the main synclinorial axis and away from the anticlinorial axis at Embury. This suggests that these major warps were developing late during the folding and causing gravity-induced movement of the tops of existing folds. It is also possible that there was some topographic expression of the major folds below. Dearman (1967) suggested flowage of minor folds down the flanks of major folds, but later (1969) seemed to relate these lesser

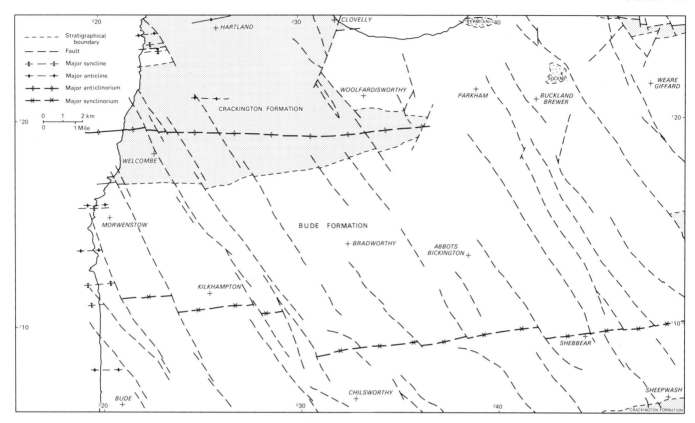

Figure 7 Structural map of the Bude district

folds to a later phase of movement. The great variability of facing direction of the minor folds makes the latter explanation unlikely.   E C F

To the north of the major Embury anticlinorium the folds are fairly consistently overturned to the north, and in some cases the north-facing limbs are inverted. Axial planes dip to the south at between 40° and 90°, averaging about 60°. The fold-profiles are mainly of zigzag or chevron type (Plate 8); interlimb angles range from 50° to 120° but most fall between 60° and 70°. Some folds with concentric (Plate 9), parallel and box-fold profiles also occur. Folds plunge to both east and west and many are periclinal.

The fold envelope undulates in a series of large periclinorial warps with wavelengths of the order of 2 km and amplitudes of 300 to 500 m. These structures produce repetition of strata, and the coast for 5.5 km northwards from Gull Rock shows only about 325 m of the succession (Figures 2 and 3). Major synclinoria are centred on Sandhole Rock [2185 2088] and Brownspear Beach [2240 2330], and anticlinoria on Mansley Rock [2220 2197] and St Catherine's Tor. A smaller synclinorium occurs at Speke's Mill Mouth, but the anticlinorium to the south is mainly faulted out.

Inland the steep northern limb of a major anticlinorial structure is defined by the outcrop of the Gull Rock Shale and the Hartland Quay Shale running from north of Docton [2460 2140] to south of Tosberry [2625 2105]. The shaly succession exposed in places to the south of this line is probably that between the Gull Rock Shale and the Embury Shale, brought up in the axial region of the fold. This anti-

clinorium seems to die out to the west; it is not aligned with the anticlinorium on the coast at Mansley Rock, even when faulting is taken into account. This is typical of these major structures which, like many of the smaller folds, are disposed *en échelon*.

Inverted beds around [2580 2220] south of Philham may lie in the steeply dipping limb of the Docton–Tosberry structure. Inverted beds are similarly associated with the steep limbs of major anticlinorial structures near Hartland Point and at Wood Rock, north-west of Clovelly (Edmonds, Williams and Taylor, 1979). The south-western end of the Wood Rock anticlinorium lies near Hartland village (Edmonds, Williams and Taylor, 1979).

Stereographic plots of poles to bedding planes in the north-west part of the district (Figure 8) indicate the general east–west trend of the folds and the tendency for the north-facing limbs to be steeper than the south-facing limbs. The mean horizontality of the folds is also brought out, suggesting that many of the plunging folds are the conical terminations of periclines. The extended maximum for the northern limbs on the western stereogram, and the isolated maximum for the inland area, may indicate a general distribution of modified folds such as those of Gull Rock Beach [2140 2005] and Nabor Beach [2140 2020] (Figure 9, p. 38) which produce gentle northerly dips. The weakness of the maximum for the northerly limbs on the stereogram of the inland area is probably accounted for by the presence of the southern flank of the Wood Rock anticlinorium, and by the general tendency for the shallow-dipping limbs of folds to predominate in random inland exposures.   RTT

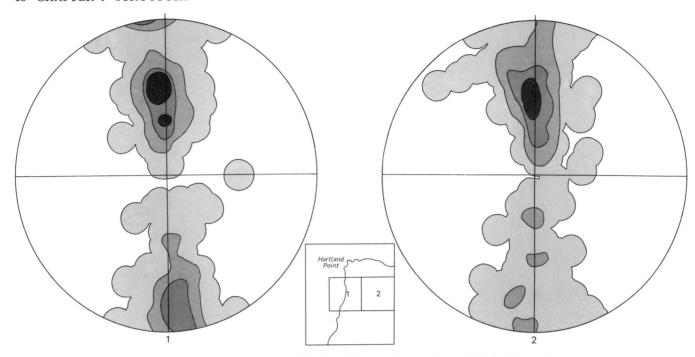

Figure 8 Stereograms of poles to bedding planes of the Crackington Formation and Bude Formation rocks of the Hartland area (see inset map): contours at 0, 3, 7 and 10 per cent

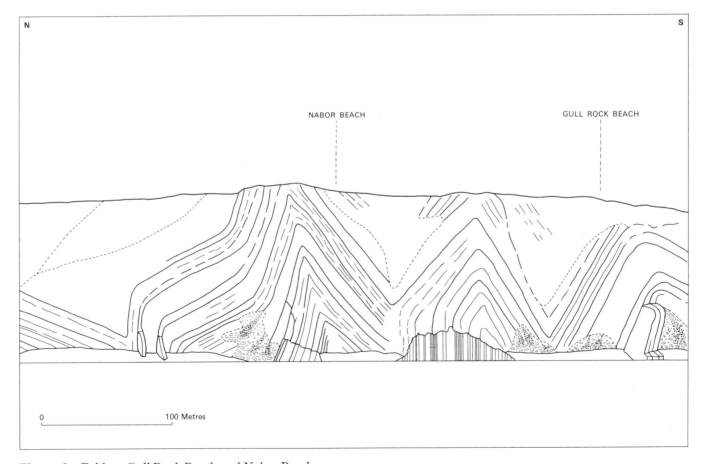

Figure 9 Folds at Gull Rock Beach and Nabor Beach

Plate 7   Anticline and syncline in Bude Formation, Henna Cliff

Sandstones, siltstones, mudstones and shales form a cliff 137 m high. The Tom's Cove Shale in the lower part of
the anticline protrudes into overlying sandstones in a cuspate structure. The Saturday's Pit Shale is exposed in the
upper part of the syncline. (A 12056).

Inland in the north-western part of the district, upright
folds predominate over folds with southward-dipping axial
planes, and the influence of the major Embury anticlinorium
and Duckpool synclinorium is less apparent. Northerly-
overturned folds are more in evidence towards the north, and
are common in the coastal section (Edmonds, Williams and
Taylor, 1979).   BJW

In the south, between Chilsworthy and Thornbury, the
orientation of fold limbs exhibit maxima at about 21°/357°,
53°/358° and vertical striking 090°. This points to the
presence of close south-facing folds. Farther east, in the area
between Cookbury and Thornbury in the west and Sheepwash and Buckland Filleigh in the east, the maxima are
about 9°/358°, 53°/360° and vertical striking 090°, indicating
slightly less southward overturning of open and close folds.
Between Bradworthy and Milton Damerel, fold limbs show
preferred orientations of 12°/352°, 45°/354° and vertical
striking 092°, with vertical dips more common than to the
south. The pattern of open and close south-facing folds
(Figure 10) persists, with southward overturning again
slightly less than in the Cookbury–Thornbury area.   EAE

FAULTS

Strike faults are uncommon, apart from minor dislocations
within the cores of folds, and in the southern part of the district
their throw rarely exceeds 50 m. In most cases such faults are
normal and dip steeply to the north. However, two faults at
Brownspear Beach near northing [2340] dip at about 70° to
the south and show a southerly downthrow of around 200 m.
These faults may be similar to those which bound the
Crediton trough of central Devon, and part of the widespread
set related to graben structures in the south of England
(Whittaker, 1975).   ECF, RTT

In the north-eastern part of the district, the only major
strike faults are the one postulated by Burne and Moore
(1971), which borders the northern edge of the Crackington
Formation, and the Portledge Fault, which throws down
Permian rocks to the south against Bude Formation.   BJW

The most prominent faults in the district are wrench
faults generally trending north-west, part of the set of faults
which traverses Devon and Cornwall (Dearman, 1963).
They lie usually less than 1 km apart in zones 2 to 3 km apart.

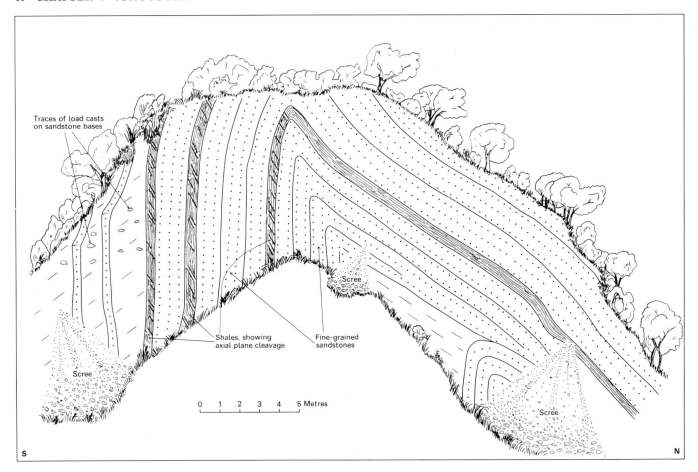

Traces of load casts on sandstone bases

Shales, showing axial plane cleavage

Fine-grained sandstones

Scree

Scree

Scree

0 1 2 3 4 5 Metres

S

N

Figure 10 Bradworthy Mill Quarry: folded Bude Formation strata

Most of these faults seen at the coast show displacements of only 1 to 2 m. However, one with an apparent vertical displacement of several hundred metres crosses the coast just south of Sandy Mouth. It appears to be the same fracture that displaces the Crackington Formation–Bude Formation junction 1.5 to 2 km dextrally in the Holsworthy district to the south.

The inland courses of these faults are commonly uncertain, but may be marked by lines of springs, fault scarps and displaced features. The general trend is between 140° and 150°. Some others running nearer to north–south show only very slight dextral movement. A subordinate set of faults trends around north-east; those seen on the coast usually show small sinistral displacements, and inland faults of this trend are impersistent.   E C F

This regional pattern of north-westerly dextral and north-easterly sinistral wrench faults, with a few strike faults, is maintained across the north-western part of the district. The dextral faults are dominant and commonly occur in groups, such as those crossing the coast between Osland Beach [2180 2080] and Elmscott Beach [2210 2145] and at Hartland Quay. A group has been traced inland and passes south-east between Burford and Highworthy [3145 2191]. Several dextral faults have in addition a westerly downthrow indicated by inclined slickensides. Sinistral faults are less common and usually have small displacements. An exten-

sive north-north-east-trending fault has been inferred along the valley of the Clifford Water. Sinistral faults occur at the coast south-east of Clovelly on the continuation of this line [3206 2462], but the amount of movement is unknown.

R T T

The same fracture pattern persists over the north-east of the district. The Sticklepath Fault is the most striking of the dextral wrench faults. It enters the district [415 250] near Winscott Barton and can be traced south-eastwards via the upper reaches of the River Yeo, Orleigh Court, and through minor valleys south of Upcott and Frithelstock, to cross a tributary of the Torridge at Watergate Bridge [4683 1752]. From there the fault follows a valley to near Smytham, where a north-easterly trending wrench fault displaces it about 0.5 km to the south-west, whence it continues south-eastwards into the Chulmleigh district. Other major north-west to south-east wrench faults run from near Newhaven [395 220] through Tythecott [414 176] to Thornehill Head [420 165]; on the southern side of the Torridge valley through Taddiport [486 185]; from near Bulkworthy [390 140] south-eastwards along the River Torridge; and from Doves Moor [417 143] to Pennicknold [442 104].   B J W

In the south and south-east of the district major faults trend between west-north-west and north-north-west from near Rhude [310 070] to Virworthy Mill [301 100], from Soldon Cross [322 105] to west of Kimworthy [311 127], from north of Holsworthy Beacon [358 083] past Thuborough Barton [348 102] and along the valley of the River Waldon to near Bradworthy [324 140], from near Cookbury [407 060] through Little Lashbrook [406 071] and South Wonford [381 089] to West Wonford [371 097], along the valley of Fishpool Lake east of Milton Damerel [384 107], along the valley of the River Torridge both downstream and upstream of the point of entry of the River Waldon [425 080], through Shebbear [439 093], and from the River Torridge west and east of Sheepwash [486 063] respectively to near Shebbear College [450 095] and along the Mussel Brook to Buckland Mill [477 086]. E A E

DETAILS

Coastal details are given southwards and northwards from the core of the Embury anticlinorium, where the lowest strata of the district are exposed, to accord with the arrangement of stratigraphical detail in Chapter 2. Minor structural details of some inland exposures given in the stratigraphical account are not repeated here.

FOLDS

Coastal section (Figure 2)

Embury Beacon [216 195]

The axis of a major asymmetric anticlinorial fold crosses the coast at Embury Beacon. The fold has a near-horizontal axis and shows a steep northern limb about 400 m long dipping at around 65° in a northerly direction. The more massive beds involved in this steep limb show little crumpling, but the incompetent Wanson Beds of Mackintosh (1965), made up of shales and thin sandstones, are thrown into violent contortions, suggesting a cascading movement down the dip of the limb (Plate 2). The southern limb of this major fold is about 1500 m long, dips at about 10° S, and bears many smaller-scale folds matching the shape of the major fold. These minor folds are well displayed, affecting the Gull Rock Shale and its attendant slumped bed on the cliffs between northings [1850] and [1950].

Welcombe Mouth to Marsland Mouth

In this section of coast there are many examples of the later recumbent folds and crumples which affect the upright folds. At northing [1790] a much-distorted anticline and syncline are visible. It is probable that the rocks were initially folded into an anticline/syncline pair with axial planes dipping at about 45° N. Later movement produced S-facing recumbent folds in the upper part of the anticline and isoclinal folding of a sandstone in the core of the syncline. The lower part of the anticline, seen at the base of the cliff, appears also to have been isoclinally folded. This structure was described by Dearman (1967). Another anticlinal structure, in this case almost upright, shows south-facing recumbent folds near its apex, at northing [1800], between the foot of the path and the waterfall at Welcombe Mouth. At northing [1822] an open anticline with limbs dipping 20° N and 25° S has a rather crumpled recumbent fold at its apex facing in a southerly direction. South of Welcombe Mouth, at around northing [1780], another open anticline with limbs dipping at 20° N and 35° S contains at its crest an angular recumbent fold facing south. On the cliff top above this there occurs a large recumbent fold whose relationship to the upright folding is obscure.

Yeol Mouth to Lucky Hole

A succession of relatively upright folds is picked out by two marker shales, the Tom's Cove Shale and the Saturday's Pit Shale. All the folds in this section have interlimb angles of 90° or more, and there is little sign of cleavage. One of the most impressive, an anticline at Henna Cliff at northing [1583], has an interlimb angle of about 130° and an axial plane dipping 80° S (Plate 7). The fold shows extensive crumpling, and a small box-shaped anticline occurs in sandstones in the centre of the fold one third of the way down from the top of the cliff. Lower down the cliff the Tom's Cove Shale in the main fold hinge has been squeezed into a cuspate structure and forced through several of the overlying sandstone beds. The Henna Cliff anticline is succeeded to the south by a syncline which shows much crumpling in its steep southern limb. At northing [1522] there is a S-facing recumbent fold about one-third of the way down the cliff on the southern flank of an anticline.

Higher Sharpnose Point to Stanbury Mouth

At northing [1440] there is a rather crumpled anticline and syncline pair showing several S-facing recumbent folds near the hinges. The main syncline lies about 50 m to the N of this locality and is somewhat box-shaped. Farther south, more S-facing recumbent folds occurring towards the apexes of upright anticlines can be seen at northings [1418] and [1388]; at the latter locality these folds are particularly well developed and about 15 to 20 m in amplitude. The upright folds and recumbent folds between Sharpnose and Hippa Rock, at northing [1375], lie in the northern limb of a major anticline with a sheet dip of about 15° N. South of Hippa Rock, near the axis of this major fold, the southern limb is overturned and dips at around 60° N, steepening to vertical at Stanbury Mouth at northing [1340]. Farther south, strata in this limb dip about 80° S towards a complex synclinal hinge around northing [1325] (Figure 2). This steep limb between Hippa Rock and Stanbury Mouth provides a continuous succession through nearly 500 m of beds.

Stanbury Mouth to Duckpool

A complex crumpled syncline is picked out just south of Stanbury Mouth by the trace of the Sandy Mouth Shale in the cliff. This shale shows intense vertical crumpling in the core of the syncline between northings [1331] and [1320], south of which it rises up the cliff towards the crest of a rather broad anticline whose vertical southern limb is seen north of Lower Sharpnose at northing [1295]. This steep limb, affected by only a few smaller folds, extends southwards to northing [1230] where several subsidiary southerly-overturned folds show unusually acute interlimb angles of around 40° to 50°. At northing [1205] a syncline shows strong crumpling and N-facing recumbent folding in its southern limb. South of the syncline lies a highly asymmetric anticline whose northern limb dips 15°–20° N and is about 500 m long. The fold axis crops out at Steeple Point, northing [1162], and a short southern limb occupies the area around Duckpool.

Duckpool to Sandy Mouth

The folds between Duckpool and Eliza Beach, around northing [1080], are characterised by interlimb angles of less than 90°. At Warren Gutter, northing [1100], shales with a few sandstones show folds with interlimb angles as tight as 35° (Plate 3). At northing [1025], north of Sandy Mouth, upright folds show interlimb angles as acute as 40°. The folds are highly asymmetric and appear to have resulted from a vertical shearing couple acting in a clockwise direction as viewed from the sea.

Sandy Mouth to Northcott Mouth

Intense faulting within this section has dismembered much of the folding and distorted many of the fold limbs. Recumbent crumpled folds and box-folds are common. A S-facing recumbent crumple occurs high on the southern flank of an anticline at northing [0968] and a large asymmetric box-fold to the south at [0955]. At northing [0932] there are some steep asymmetric and rather tight folds somewhat similar to those north of Sandy Mouth. In this case, however, the steep shearing couple appears to have acted in an anticlockwise direction. Between northings [0930] and [0923] a

large box-shaped syncline, with strong recumbent folding on its southern flank, faces south. The most impressive box-fold of this stretch of coast is an anticline at northing [0911]; the flanks are almost vertical and the top of the fold is near-horizontal but slightly collapsed (Plate 1). Another asymmetrical box-fold occurs at Menachurch Point, northing [0880]; the northern limb of the anticline dips about 60°–70° N, the top dips about 20° S and the southern limb is overturned and dips about 80° N. This fold is succeeded to the south by a crumpled syncline showing traces of N-facing recumbent folds in its southern limb.

Northcott Mouth to Bude

Rather open folds, upright or overturned to the north, extend southwards to around northing [0810]. Farther south the folds are overturned to the south. Some signs of box-folding can be seen in a syncline at around northing [0765].

Bude to Efford Cliff

The folds in this section are mainly overturned to the south. Their interlimb angles are usually less than 90°, and commonly around 50°. Some signs of box-folding are evident within a syncline at around northing [0628]. E C F

Gull Rock Beach [2140 2005] to Elmscott Beach

The northerly dipping limb of the Embury anticlinorium extends to Gull Rock Beach, where it contains the Gull Rock Shale dipping 60°/358°. The folds on Gull Rock Beach, and on Nabor Beach to the north, are large flexures with amplitudes of 100 to 120 m and with northern limbs dipping more steeply than southern. The folds have essentially zigzag profiles but the anticlines have 'cranked' northern limbs. An asymmetrical box profile is displayed at Gull Rock Beach, and an anticlinal/synclinal chair-shaped profile (Figure 9) at Nabor Beach. These modifications of the folds may be a result of their position on the steep northern limb of the major Embury structure. The anticline and syncline at Gull Rock Beach plunge about 4° W at beach level. The folds on Nabor Beach are nearly horizontal.

To the north of Nabor Beach two overturned anticlines show axial planes dipping 40°–50° S and inverted northern limbs. The fold at [2157 2038] has a northern limb dipping 82°/172° and a southern limb dipping 30°/172°.

Periclinal syncline and anticline fold pairs, in which the axes merge as the folds die out, are seen on the foreshore at [2156 2050] and [2170 2060].

A series of more open and symmetrical folds occurs between Osland Beach [2180 2080] and Elmscott Beach. The anticline at Sandhole Rock [2184 2086] has limbs dipping 55°/187° and 52°/356° and plunges about 5° W. At the northern end of Sandhole Beach open basin-like parallel folds occur with limbs dipping north and south at 16° to 24°.

Elmscott Beach to Hole Rock

A major asymmetrical anticline at Cow Rock [2227 2162] (Plate 9) brings the Gull Rock Shale to beach level. A southerly-downthrowing strike fault in the hinge appears to be an accommodation structure related to the fold movement. The limbs of the fold dip 24°/166° and 80°/350° and the plunge is at a low angle to the east. The syncline to the north is near-horizontal. The next anticline to the north has a profile similar to that at Cow Rock, but the intervening syncline is a typical chevron fold. To the north the folds have typical zigzag and chevron profiles.

Plate 8   Zigzag folds in Crackington Formation, Gunpath Beach

Axial planes dip steeply southwards. The Hartland Quay Shale is visible near the cliff top in the hinges of the anticlines; it is overlain by a thick bed of sandstone. (A 12042).

Anticlines to the south [2220 2191] and north [2220 2207] of Mansley Rock expose the Gull Rock Shale. The southern anticline plunges 9°/101°; that to the north appears to be more periclinal in form and the dips on its flanks of 35°/162° and 68°/141° indicate that it is nearly horizontal.

Northwards to Hole Rock the folds all plunge to the east. An anticline at [2223 2222] has limbs dipping 45°/162° and 68°/356° and plunges 10°/083°. Particularly fine examples of chevron folds are exposed in the cliffs at Gunpath Beach [2220 2240] (Plate 8); they are slightly overturned to the north. The anticline at [2224 2249] has limbs dipping 45°/154° and 82°/360° and plunges 19°/084°.   RTT

Inland exposures

Welcombe to Strocksworthy [341 198]

In a stream at [2358 1900] siltstones, thin sandstones and shales are folded into an anticline plunging at 20°/260°. Another stream section [2423 1889 to 2470 1860] shows many reversals of dip in shales with thin sandstones, indicating the presence of a large number of small folds; southerly dips of between 30° and 50° are common, along with northerly dips of 70° to 80°, indicating that the folds are overturned to the north.

Morwenstow to Hardsworthy [286 163]

Opposing dips in a stream section [2060 1542 to 2100 1551] indicate the presence of an anticline. Farther east another stream

[2405 1607 to 2406 1600] reveals an anticline/syncline pair; dips successively farther southward are 60°/180°, 65°/325°, and 65°/160°, indicating a syncline plunging at 30°/250° and an anticline to the south plunging at 16°/244°. Further anticlines and synclines may be detected in a nearby stream [2428 1619; 2441 1555; 2440 1542]. The more northerly anticlines are more or less upright, while those to the south are overturned to the south. In a small stream between [2888 1653] and [2820 1669] the succession of dips and strikes indicates the presence of an upright anticline and syncline affected by a recumbent S-facing crumple.

Woodford [219 133] *to Heatham* [248 129]

In a stream [2238 1339] east of Woodford sandstones and shales show opposing dips of 50°/350° and 25°/180°, indicating the presence of an anticline overturned to the north, and in a quarry [2236 1306] to the south an anticline in massive sandstones has limbs dipping 85° and 55° S. In streams near Heatham [2412 1293; 2439 1319] folding is revealed by opposing dips. At the first locality these are 45° N and 60°/175°, and at the second 55°/345° and 70°/165°; thus both folds show some overturning towards the south.

Duckpool to Lymsworthy [268 102]

Exposures at the side of forestry tracks between [2208 1150] and [2240 1137] display two anticline/syncline pairs in shales, siltstones and sandstones. The two northern folds are upright while the southern folds are overturned slightly to the north. The interlimb angles of the northern folds are less than 90°, and in one place

Plate 9 Anticline in Crackington Formation, Elmscott Gutter

A large concentric anticline shows a minor normal fault in its hinge. The Gull Rock Shale is exposed in the hinge at beach level. Elmscott Gutter, the gully to the right, has developed along a small fault. (A 12044).

less than 50°; in one of the southern folds the angle is 110°. A stream section [2237 1191] shows opposing dips of 25°/170° and 15°/345°, indicating a syncline. Others show a small anticline plunging 15° E [2232 1145], and opposing dips of 80°/170° and 20°/150° in a syncline [2527 1011]. This latter fold can be traced to the vicinity of Lymsworthy, where beds dip 80°/160° [2686 1022] and 40°/010° [2704 1014].

Lower Northcott [214 087] to Pigsdon [280 090]

Two small anticlines are exposed in an old quarry [2140 0876]; the limbs dip 55° N and 60°/200°. In a stream section [2487 0821] a small anticline plunges at 10°/080°; the southern limb dips 80°/170°. A short distance upstream [2496 0817] opposing dips of 40°/340° and 85°/165° indicate the presence of an anticline. The same section [2512 0773] shows dips of 80°/340°, inverted, and, immediately to the north, 20°/350°, normal, suggesting the presence of a small anticline strongly overturned towards the south. A quarry [2767 0936] near Lower Pickington exposes a succession of massive sandstones and shales folded into an anticline trending 075° with the northern limb dipping at 30°/345° and the southern limb dipping at 45° to 50° southwards.

Stratton to Grimscott

A major anticline is suggested by opposing dips of 39°/350° and 30°/200° in a roadside section [2314 0671]. Dips of 20°/340° and 40°/180° in a stream to the east [2366 0674] probably mark the same fold. The same stream [2363 0684] has exposed a small anticline and complementary syncline. The presence of many anticlines and synclines can be inferred in stream exposures between [2592 0721] and [2565 0684]; at one place [2587 0711] a syncline shows limbs dipping 40°/175° and 75°/350°.   E C F

Parkham to Buckland Brewer

Small-scale folds trending 080° are exposed in a stream bed [3806 2207 to 3810 2215] south of Foxdown in thinly bedded sandstones. They have a wavelength of about 5 m, and the limbs dip at 50° to 60°. Farther east [4350 2075], in the valley of the River Duntz, medium-bedded sandstones with shaly partings are folded into an anticline plunging 10°/250°. The limbs dip 40°/340° and 30°/170°.

West Putford to Langtree

In the bed of the Weasel Water, near Mambury, medium-bedded sandstones dip 40°/345° [3838 1608] and 45°/165° [3842 1600], suggesting an open upright anticline. In a tributary of the Lydeland

Water [4091 1906] thickly bedded sandstones are vertical, striking 080°, and poorly exposed sandstones in the stream bed 50 m to the S suggest the presence of an asymmetric anticline with a vertical northern limb. At Watergate Bridge a small quarry [4684 1763] contains an E–W-trending asymmetric anticline, with limbs dipping 80° N and 65° S.

Torridge valley, Great Torrington to Weare Gifford

In Beam Quarry [471 204] sandstones and shales are folded into an asymmetric anticline plunging 5°/095° with limbs dipping 25°–40°/010° and 45°/185°. A roadside quarry [4706 2088] farther north reveals an upright open anticline in thickly bedded sandstones, with limbs dipping 50°/355° and 45°/175°. Another quarry [4722 2099], 300 m N of Beam Mansion, shows a northward-overturned anticline and syncline trending 100°. Farther north [4659 2187], a northerly-overturned anticline trends 045°.

Bulkworthy to Peters Marland

Exposures near Eastbridge, in thinly bedded sandstones and shales, suggest an open syncline trending 075° [4015 1290]. Both limbs dip at 50°. In the bed of the River Torridge [414 109] small-scale folds with an amplitude of about 3 m strike E–W and appear to be overturned to the north. Some 400 m E of Allisland a syncline exposed in a stream strikes 030° in thinly bedded sandstones, both limbs dipping at 70°.   BJW

Lana to Cookbury Moor

In a small disused quarry [3377 0694] east-south-east of Babington the core of an anticline in sandstones, silty sandstones and silty shales is exposed; the limbs dip 45°/010° and 20°/210°. Similar strata exposed alongside the old canal [3376 0633] 600 m to the S are horizontal, and another outcrop beside the same canal [3415 0592] south-west of Hogs Park exhibits beds dipping 35°/310° and gently to the north.

A stream section [3776 0737 to 3781 0732] 650 m WSW of Woodacott shows fold limbs dipping 25°/345° and vertically, strike 100°. Sandstones in an old pit [3842 0658] alongside this stream farther downstream are cut by steep to vertical joints trending N–S.

Cookbury to Highweek

The valley-side [4098 0589] immediately east of Cookbury shows sandstones affected by bedding-plane slip and dipping 40°/330° and 20°/180°, suggesting an open upright anticline.

Near the head of a small valley [4238 0586] at Hole, strata dip vertically, strike 090°, on the south side of a NW–SE fault, and 45°/025° and 20°/345° on the north side. Immediately upstream [4234 0579 to 4237 0582], dips within a group of sandstones range up to 75° to both north and south.

An old quarry face [4391 0640] just south of Dippermill shows sandstones dipping 30°/010° high in the face and steepening to 80°/010° nearer the quarry floor.

Libbear Barton to Sheepwash

Vertical beds striking 350° in the stream course [4527 0709] north of Libbear Barton, within a section [4522 0712 to 4529 0707] generally showing steep and gentle northerly dips, probably owe their alignment to the effects of a NW–SE fault coursing along the valley.

Closely adjacent dips recorded in a stream valley farther east indicate folds with limbs inclined 5°/005° and vertical, strike 095° [4645 0734], 10°/360° and vertical, strike 090° [4631 0690], and

20°/350° and vertical, strike 075° [4634 0677]. The association of gentle northerly dips with vertical beds striking E–W (20°/330°–340° and vertical strike 100°–110°) is repeated in a stream course [4755 0585 to 4762 0578] east of Black Torrington.

Old sandstone quarries west of Sheepwash Bridge show mainly northerly dips of 20°–60°, but also an open anticline [4853 0571] whose axis trends 120° immediately south of a strike fault.

Dunsdon to Barrow

Shales, siltstones and sandstones cropping out at Slade [312 083] lie within an anticline whose limbs dip 45°/360° and 75°/170°. A stream to the north-east [3186 0868] cuts through strata exhibiting moderate (40°–45°) and steep (75°–85°) northerly dips, indicating close folds slightly overturned to the south.

In an old sandstone quarry [3323 0757] between Ugworthy and Vognacott strata dipping 40°/180° lie between vertical beds striking 100°, delineating a syncline and anticline slightly overturned to the north.

Holsworthy Beacon to Shebbear

Exposures in Thorne Wood, north-west of Thornbury, show shales, siltstones and thin sandstones striking 100°, dipping 30°–90°/010° and showing traces of gentle minor folding [3975 0878]. A stream-side quarry [4034 0999] 750 m N of Thornbury Mill shows, in a newly dug east bay, sandstones with subordinate shales and silt-stones dipping 10°–25°/320°–340°. The section is cut by strike faults and the strata exhibit traces of gentle folding (Figure 4).

A quarry [4368 0950] at Pitt, on the northern outskirts of Shebbear, shows, in its western face, sandstones with shales and siltstones cut by four E–W strike faults (Figure 5). The strata lie within a gentle anticline, whose axis trends approximately E–W, and are crumpled between the faults. The east face lies just north of the projected lines of the faults, and shows an anticline whose limbs dip 30°/360° and 25°/130°. In the north face the beds dip 30°/360°, and traces of bottom structures show them to be right way up.

Battledown Cross to Filleigh Moor

An outcrop [4740 0986] in the valley of the Mussel Brook comprises fine- to medium-grained thickly bedded sandstones containing ovoids of weathered friable micaceous medium-grained sandstone; in small exposures the latter resemble fold noses, but in most cases this is illusory.

In the neighbourhood of Filleigh Moor, the Newcourt Water cuts through shales with thin sandstones locally disposed in tight upright folds whose limbs dip 80°/020° and 85°/190° [4893 0825].

Virworthy to Sutcombe

Close and open upright folds are exposed in the stream [3137 1039] at Virworthy. A small laneside quarry [3273 1195] 400 m E of Instaple has been opened in what appears to be a southward-overturned anticline whose limbs dip 25°/010° and 70°/360°.

Southerly dips in the area around and south of Sutcombemill [3476 1068; 3462 1089; 3482 1118] are probably associated with upright folds.

Bradworthy area

A gentle syncline in sandstones [3175 1499] north-east of Spittle has limbs dipping 10°/190° and 10°/350°. About 650 m to the S, on either side of the River Waldon, lie the two bays of Bradworthy Mill Quarry of E.C.C. Quarries Ltd. In the west bay [3180 1435] an anticline exhibits a N-dipping axial plane which steepens from 65° to 80° (Figure 10). The southern limb is near-vertical, strike

090°; it shows traces of load-casts on the bases of sandstone beds, and axial-plane cleavage cutting shale bands. The fold axis trends 080°, and the strata of the northern limb dip at various, but generally moderate, angles northwards. On the opposite side of the valley the east bay [3192 1436] is cut in the steep or vertical southern limb, and well-developed load-casts are visible high in the south-east corner.

Farther down-river, on the eastern bank 150 m SE of Waterland Mill, an old quarry [3305 1295] exposes vertical sandstone beds; prominent load-casts on the south face indicate younging to the south.

Upcott to Milton Damerel

Minor folding in a small stream course [3636 1007] 600 m SW of Waldon Bridge exhibits an axial trend of 085°.

An old pit [3918 1021] 350 m WSW of Gratton shows shales, siltstones and silty sandstones overlying thickly bedded sandstone. The shales are locally rust-spotted after pyrite, and the beds are cut by a near-vertical fault trending slightly N of E.   E A E

FAULTS

Coastal section

Embury Beacon to Bude

E–W faults are exposed as follows: at Stanbury Mouth, at northing [1331], a vertical fault throws down less than 10 m N; at Sandy Mouth, at northing [0995], a fault dips 55° S and throws down 15 m S; at West Park Pit, northing [0895], a fault dips 75° N and shows a downthrow of about 30 m N; at Northcott Mouth, at northing [0858], a fault trending 080° and dipping 75° N can be shown by matching shale bands to have a downthrow of 60 m N.

NW–SE faults are more common. At Knaps Longpeak several faults trending 150° cut the base of the cliff at northings [1900], [1895], [1886] and [1884]; the fault at northing [1895] shows a dextral shift of 12 m. Near Marsland Mouth, between northings [1732] and [1730], an extensive zone of faulting, with great disturbance, trends 155°–160°. The movement was apparently dextral, but of unknown extent. Correlation of the Hartland Quay Shale across the fault zone shows that there has been little disruption of the stratigraphy to north and south. At Higher Sharpnose Point, at northing [1485], a fault trends 160° and shows a dextral terminal drag, but displacement is only a few metres. At northing [1282], on Lower Sharpnose Point, a fault trending 140° shows signs of dextral movement and truncates the Sandy Mouth Shale. A sand-filled slack just offshore, visible on aerial photographs, probably marks the site of the Sandy Mouth Shale on the northern side of the fault, indicating a dextral shift of about 80 m. At Duckpool, between northings [1130] and [1115], faults with a general trend of 150° show many signs of dextral terminal drag; the amount of displacement is not known, but is probably small. Farther south other small dextral faults trending between 140° and 150° occur at northings [1084], [1074] and [1020]. Near Sandy Mouth a zone of faulting trending 150° crosses the cliff line between northings [0987] and [0975] and truncates the outcrop of the Sandy Mouth Shale on its north-east side. Terminal drag indicates a dextral shift, but the amount of displacement is unknown. Extrapolations of the thicknesses of strata above and below the Sandy Mouth Shale suggest that the displacement may be several hundred metres, and an 800-m displacement of the Crackington Formation–Bude Formation junction near Bridgerule [277 010] in the Holsworthy district may mark the south-eastward continuation of this fracture zone. South of Sandy Mouth a small wrench

fault at northing [0936] trends 150° and shows a dextral displacement of between 5 and 8 m. A fault trending 165° cuts Menachurch Point at northings [1876] and [1833] and appears to have combined some vertical movement with a small sinistral horizontal shift. Several faults at Northcott Mouth trend around 150° and cut the cliff at northing [0842]; one shows a dextral shift of 10 m. A very pronounced fault trends 160° near Crooklets Beach at Bude: it runs from [2002 0734] south-eastwards under the outer wall of the Saturday's Pit Swimming Pool [2022 0677] and shows a dextral displacement of 50 m.   E C F

Nabor Beach to Longpeak

On Nabor Beach [2140 2020] two small dextral faults trend NW–SE. The southern fault shows a maximum displacement of about 0.6 m and dies out as it crosses on to Gull Rock Beach to the south. The northern fault, with a lateral displacement of some 3.5 m, displays slickensides plunging 40° NW, indicating an oblique movement with a downthrow component to the south-west. Both faults dip steeply to the south-west. A minor dextral fault at [2161 2055] has a lateral displacement of about 3.5 m, dips 60° SW and dies out south-eastwards.

On Osland Beach [2175 2080] a NW–SE dextral fault bifurcates and displaces fold axes 16.50 m on its western branch and 2.75 m on its eastern branch. Minor dextral faults on Sandhole Beach [2185 2098 and 2192 2121] have produced a reddened fault breccia with a dolomitic cement.

On Elmscott Beach [2210 2145] two faults trend NW–SE. The southern fault dips 75° SW and the northern 50° SW. These faults probably mark fairly large dextral displacements. Their general line can be traced to the south-east for about 1.5 km by means of surface features.

Minor strike faults occur in Elmscott Gutter [2228 2155] and in the hinge of the anticline at Cow Rock [2227 2162]; the latter shows a southerly downthrow of about 5 m. This fracture probably represents an accommodation movement in the hinge of the fold, as the displacement appears to decrease downwards. South of Longpeak [2217 2294] a small strike fault intersects with a small sinistral fault.   R T T

Inland exposures

Welcombe to Ashmansworthy

A stream section [2425 1881] shows deflection of bedding by terminal drag associated with a fault trending 150°. Farther inland a line of springs and wet patches between [2755 1862] and [2783 1814] indicates the presence of a NW–SE wrench fault. Other lines of springs and seepages indicating faults trending around 150° occur between [3169 1912] and [3246 1810], and at the south-east end of this fracture zone many sandstone features are truncated. A similar line of springs occurs to the east, trending 150° between [3321 1948] and [3388 1834].

Shop

A fault exposed in a stream at [2346 1368] trends 140° and dips 75° NE. The amount of movement is unknown but is probably mainly dextral with some normal vertical movement. The same fault produces springs to the north-west [2305 1442].

Kilkhampton

Near Kilkhampton, in a stream section [2502 1031], rotation of sandstone beds by terminal drag suggests the presence of a fault trending 148°. South of Kilkhampton, in another stream [2448

0920], a small fault trends 120°, dips 60° NE and shows components of both dextral and normal movement.

Grimscott

Stream-course exposures [2535 0833] show rotation of strike, and many springs emerge along the valley. This suggests that the stream has followed a fault trending 055°. A similar combination of outcrops [2566 0688] and springs suggest a fault trending 142°; nearby in the same stream [2568 0678] a small splay fault trends 110° and dips 85° E.

Pigsdon

A small fault exposed in a stream [2884 0960] trends 120° and dips 80° N. This fault shows both normal and dextral movement.

Kingford

A small stream [2919 0616] exposes rather soft sandstone beds with their strike rotated into a NE–SW alignment by a fault trending 035° along the stream. ECF

Buckland Brewer

Near Buckland Brewer a fault trending 010° displaces two shale bands [422 225 and 421 219] sinistrally for about 100 m.

Monkleigh

Two shale bands [455 206 and 458 202] are each displaced 100 m in a dextral sense by a fault trending 145°. A fault trending 157° displaces a shale band dextrally by 80 m [468 211]. BJW

Cookbury to Highweek

South of the River Torridge micaceous sandstones and siltstones dipping 20°–45°/330°–360° are cut by a fault trending 090° [4623 0592].

Holsworthy Beacon to Thornbury

Shales and sandstones at Down [3712 0878] dip up to 50° N and are cut by a N–S fault. Exposures in Thorne Wood, north-west of Thornbury, show shales with silty nodules and thin sandstones dipping 20°–30°/355° and cut by two NW-trending faults [3967 0877].

Battledown Cross to Filleigh Moor

Sandstones, siltstones and shales in a small old quarry [4611 0799] south-east of Lovacott show slickensides related to slip on bedding planes. Probably the movement was associated with the NW–SE fault which runs along the valley 120 m to the E.

Upcott to Milton Damerel

Fairly massive sandstone in an old quarry [3720 1192] east of Great Derworthy is locally stained red and is cut by thin quartz veins and near-horizontal fractures. A disused sandstone quarry [386 114] south of Horrellsford contains some sandstone breccia and vein quartz, probably reflecting the proximity of the fault which runs NNW along the valley of the Fishpool Lake 50 m to the W. EAE

CHAPTER 5

Pleistocene and Recent

INTRODUCTION

Little evidence is available to help in correlating the superficial deposits of the district. Surveys farther north (Edmonds, 1972; Edmonds, Williams and Taylor, 1979) lead to the conclusion that the 1st Terrace of the River Torridge equates with the raised beach and is of Ipswichian age. Higher river terraces are also probably mainly or wholly Upper Pleistocene. Head developed mainly during Devensian times and alluvium in Recent times. Boulders at Shebbear are of unknown age. Dates of river chronology are largely unknown, except that in early Tertiary times the present lower reaches of the River Torridge flowed south and south-eastwards to the Exe (Edmonds, 1972).

River terraces are not extensively developed and except in the lower reaches of the River Torridge correlation over appreciable distances is impossible. However, small scattered raised flats of silty clay occur along most of the stream valleys, and somewhat wider tracts near the confluence of the River Waldon with the Torridge. The flood-plain alluvium of the district comprises brown silts and clays with irregular developments of gravel; all the material is of local origin.

The main stretch of the River Torridge in the district follows roughly its ancestral (early Tertiary) course. The lower reaches, around Torrington, then flowed southwards to join this flow *en route* to the early River Exe, but underwent reversal before deposition of the sediments of the Petrockstow Basin (Edmonds, 1972; Freshney, Beer and Wright, 1979).

Minor stream captures may have occurred near the coast, but most of the drainage changes there have stemmed from marine erosion cutting back into river channels.

Terraces between Brendon and Cookbury Moor Plantation (p. 50) indicate an easterly flow in early Upper Pleistocene times, as at present. Possibly, however, flow continued eastwards through the present saddle south of Bradford [4210 0725] until diverted northwards by capture. Wide terrace flats south of Blagdonmoor Wharf [361 058], just outside the district, now border a very small southwesterly flowing stream. The form of the terraces is not clearly indicative of a direction of flow, and it seems likely that the flats correlate with those nearby at Brendon. Thus in early Upper Pleistocene times the Blagdonmoor Wharf stream probably flowed north-eastwards to join the Brendon stream, the River Waldon and the Torridge.

As is usual in most of south-west England, the Bude district carries a superficial cover of heterogeneous sediment, generally stony sandy clay, whose nature reflects the local lithologies. Some is a residual weathering product, some has moved downslope in the course of freeze-thaw cycles of late Pleistocene times. In general the two are indistinguishable one from the other, and both are classified as Head.

Sandstone-rich Head is characteristic of the sandstone ridges in the south-east and north-east of the district, and of the extensive tracts of fine-grained sandstone elsewhere. More clayey Head is present where the bedrock is predominantly shaly, but much sandy debris has washed down from sandstone ridges into shaly hollows and the distinction is not sharp. Head-free areas are not common and are mainly confined to the tops of ridges, the steeper hillsides and the banks of deeply incised rivers and streams.　　　　ᴇᴀᴇ

The Head cover is particularly well developed to the east of the watershed between the short coastal streams and the headwaters of the rivers Torridge and Tamar. In this area the landscape is subdued and mature, with slow-moving streams feeding the Torridge and Tamar; little erosion of the Head has taken place and it may be up to 3 or 4 m thick. The deposit comprises clayey sand and sandy clay and bears little detailed relationship to the underlying solid rocks.

To the west of the watershed the streams have steeper profiles, erosion is more intense, and only remnants of Head remain. Most occurs on the flanks of the hills and on the valley sides, and it is highly variable in thickness. Many prominent east–west ridges have little Head along their crests, this being particularly true near the cliff line. In this area the Head is less mature than to the east and contains much sandstone and shale debris set in a sandy clay matrix.

Blown sand covers a small area at Northcott Mouth, and a much larger one on Summerleaze Down and Bude golf course. It is derived directly from the beach sand, and although the dunes on the golf course have been stabilised and grassed over, blown sand is still accumulating at the present day.　　　　ᴇᴄғ

Extensive landslip occurs on the coast in the area of Sandhole Cliff. The main cause of instability here seems to be the presence of the group of dextral faults passing northwestwards through the cliff. The most northerly of these faults effectively defines the limit of the slipped area. Dixons Well [2225 2115] is an area of slipped strata in which part of the cliff top has settled between two faults with only a small amount of rotational movement.

Other areas of landslip occur below Osland Pits [2195 2068] and north of Nabor Point [2160 2030]. Small areas of landslip in which the cores of synclines at the tops of the cliffs have collapsed seawards are quite common on the coast south of Hole Rock.　　　　ʀᴛᴛ

Two large boulders at Shebbear are of a rock type unmatched in the district. The first is the famous 'Devil's Stone' [4388 0924], which lies near the church and is turned over as part of an annual ritual on the night of November 5th. In hand specimen it is a coarse quartz grit. The second lies embedded in the road verge [4381 1001] north of the village; it is a similar rock type, but the boulder is probably much bigger than the 'Devil's Stone'.

Mr R. W. Sanderson reports that specimens from the two rocks (E 44148–9) are of similar lithology, the northern one

(E 44149) being coarser grained and less iron-stained. Both are conglomeratic orthoquartzites of textural immaturity. Subangular pebbles up to 7 mm (E 44148) and 18 mm (E 44149) across, mostly of metamorphic quartz or quartzite, occur with rare small chert fragments in a matrix of quartz grains. All are set in a cement of secondary overgrowths of silica which is variably stained by iron oxide and in places is opaque. Detrital mineral grains are rare and small and include zircon, locally euhedral, and lesser amounts of blue-green amphibole, brown tourmaline and muscovite.

There are three possible explanations of the presence of these boulders. The first is that they were brought by primitive men, but while this could well be true of a rock the size and roughly tabular shape of the Devil's Stone, if it had great value, there seems little likelihood of the second boulder, large, irregular and enormously heavy, having been manhandled to its present position.

The second possibility is transport by ice. Not Devensian ice, whose southern limit, although a matter of dispute, lay north of the district; and probably not Wolstonian ice, which left a legacy of thick boulder clay at Fremington and appears not to have penetrated far inland. However it is worth recalling that a small erratic of pebbly quartzite has been recorded (Edmonds, 1972) from the Fremington till. An earlier, perhaps Anglian, ice sheet may have advanced across south-west England, but the Shebbear boulders lie at 143 and 168 m OD and a glaciation of this magnitude must surely have left signs too numerous to have been totally concealed by Head.

Excavations for the M5 Motorway about 3 km S of Taunton revealed a boulder of quartzitic fine-grained sandstone which Mr R. K. Harrison described as showing an overall mineralogical resemblance to the Shebbear specimens, although finer grained. However, the Shebbear lithologies have not been matched. Mr Sanderson notes that the least dissimilar rocks occur in the coarser parts of the Millstone Grit of South Wales, but the possibility exists of a source now on the sea-bed.

The third possibility is that the boulders represent the remains of strata now removed by denudation, and the most likely age for such rocks is Tertiary. This theory is open to the objection that a widespread cover would have left more debris, even if only scattered concretionary bodies were strong enough to survive for long.

Clearly there is no conclusive explanation. Action by men is the least likely main mechanism. An ice sheet advancing from Wales across central Devon is unlikely to have left, as its only large exposed erratics, two boulders of similar rock type close to one another and unmatched in the area traversed by the ice. Thus we are left with the third possibility, the suggestion that a ?Tertiary cover, perhaps differentially cemented, now remains visible only as two boulders. Such an explanation does not, of course, preclude the chance that the stones may have been moved short distances by local ice which developed on high ground south of the main ice sheets, or that one of them may have acquired some ceremonial significance and been manhandled to its present site.   EAE

DETAILS

RIVER TERRACES

Western area

The rivers of the western part of the district drain from a watershed which follows approximately the line of the A39 road. Those to the west of this watershed occupy steep narrow valleys with poorly developed terraces in their upper and middle reaches; active downcutting near their mouths has also left narrow remnants of terrace on the valley sides. Some of the streams, such as the Tidna near Morwenstow, have not succeeded in cutting down to sea level and emerge at the coast in hanging valleys with waterfalls but no terrace deposits.

The stream which reaches the sea at Welcombe Mouth traverses a narrow alluvial strip down to about [217 183], beyond which it has cut down leaving gravels at two levels above it. In the cliffs [2125 1798] about 7.5 m of well-rounded gravel rest on sandstone and shale and probably belong to the 1st Terrace. A short distance upstream [2145 1812] occur 2.1 m of yellow-brown clayey gravel of the 2nd Terrace. Similarly isolated patches of gravel [e.g. 2020 1156] lie several metres above a stream at Duckpool, but pass upstream into alluvium at Combe Mill [2095 1170].

The larger streams and rivers in the Bude area, such as the River Neet, have gentler gradients than the coastal streams to the north and are more mature. All have well-developed alluvial flats and some terraces occur, the best developed being in the valley between Stratton and Diddies [236 064] where the terrace level is 2 to 3 m above the river. The river has cut through the thin alluvium into Head and locally into bedrock. The terrace runs into alluvium upstream of a knick point at Diddies. Small patches of terrace 0.3 to 0.6 m above the general level of the alluvium occur in the valley of the River Neet at Poughill Mill [2308 0738], and above Bush at [2350 0815].

River Tamar

A small patch of 1st Terrace north of Blatchborough shows [2814 1482] 0.3 m of yellowish orange silty clay overlain by 0.45 m of brown and orange gravelly clay. Terraces are common around Pancrasweek, as at [281 077], but show no sections. South-west of Kingford a small terrace flat bears a few scattered subrounded pebbles [2835 0580]. A tributary of the River Tamar north of the Lamberal Water is bordered by a few narrow strips of terrace, as at [2757 1040].

River Torridge and tributaries

The upper Torridge between Brimford Bridge [282 172] and Ashmansworthy [340 172] has very few distinct terrace flats, although many gentle clayey slopes bordering the river may represent degraded terraces. Such slopes are particularly evident south of Gorvin around [291 189]. A more obvious terrace flat to the south [294 185] forms wet and clayey ground and shows no sections. Other clayey flats occur farther downstream at [309 177], [315 182] and [349 171], the last being just over 2 m above river level.   ECF

A small patch of stony sandy clay occurs on the south bank of the Torridge [359 165] at Cory. Its top is about 3 m above the alluvium and the back of the flat is poorly defined. A marshy gently sloping silty clay flat [370 146] borders the alluvium east of Julian's Putford; its back is at 122 m OD. Farther downstream a 1-km strip of terrace deposit lies on the north-east side of the alluvium [411 113 to 418 107], with the back of the flat at about 100 m.   BJW

Curiously, the largest terrace flats in the south-east occur along the headwater stretches of the unnamed stream which flows east from Brendon [362 074] to Cookbury Moor Plantation [396 064], and in the headwater area immediately south of Blagdonmoor Wharf [361 058] just outside the present district. It seems likely that these occurrences, which lie fairly close together, are the products of a drainage pattern different from the present one. Headwater flats near Brendon, 3.5 km long [362 070 to 398 066] and up to 500 m wide, are disposed in two terraces of wet silty clay with scattered rushes. The back of the higher terrace falls from 145 to 114 m OD, that of the lower from 137 to 107.

Small terrace remnants of silty clay occur alongside the headwaters of the River Waldon west of Bradworthy at 160 m OD [319 141] and north of Soldon Manor at 152 to 145 m OD [328 112 to 333 113]. Farther downstream, and in small tributary valleys, terrace flats of clay and silt occur north-west of Waldon at 129 m OD [366 111], near Miltonmill Bridge at 114 m [375 103], north of Down at 145 to 137 m [368 091 to 375 092] and west of Thornbury at 137 m [392 084]. Larger terrace flats border the river as follows: 150 m wide, with back at about 111 m OD [389 097]; 100 m wide at 99 m [403 097]; 60 m wide at 100 m [405 090; 406 086]. The most extensive terrace of the River Waldon occurs at its confluence with the Torridge; a bench of silt and clay up to 200 m wide stretches for 1.5 km [412 084 to 427 083] and rises to about 100 m OD

Few terraces are preserved alongside the River Torridge in the south-east of the district. Small flats occur in some of the tributary valleys as follows: east of Holroyd House at 99 m OD [451 073]; north-west of Gortleigh at 91 m [463 068]; sporadically along the Mussel Brook at 102 to 184 m [475 100 to 479 077]. In the extreme south-east corner of the district a 250-m-wide terrace flat of silty clay [492 060] bordering the Torridge is traversed by vaguely defined features which may mark ancient river courses or may divide the flat into two terraces differing very little in altitude. The back of the whole flat is at 68 m OD. E A E

Downstream from Great Torrington small tracts of the 1st Terrace occur at [480 194], [479 196], [477 200], [476 204] and [472 207]. None rises more than 3 m above the alluvium, and in the last two localities a low rock bench separates the deposit from the higher 2nd Terrace. The 2nd Terrace deposits consist of stony clays and silts with gravelly courses composed of rounded sandstone pebbles. Two exposures of the 2nd Terrace near Weare Giffard, around [474 215] and [463 224], show a similar composition. B J W

South-flowing streams of Holsworthy Hamlets

Silty clay flats whose backs rise to 129 m OD occur to the west [309 083] and south-east [316 079] of Slade. The eastern flat is up to 160 m wide. Similar terrace remnants lie farther downstream [305 073; 305 071] east of Lana, at about 122 m OD.

Similar, generally narrow, benches of silty clay border streams north and north-north-east of Chilsworthy at 137 to 145 m OD [327 083 to 333 079; 341 084 to 343 079] and about 128 m OD [330 071; 331 067].

Just south-east of Hogs Park, on the southern edge of the district, a headwater stream flows through a silty bench [342 058 to 349 061] up to 200 m wide and about 3 m above present stream level. The wide alluvium/terrace flats of Blagdonmoor Wharf are only 1 km to the east. E A E

HEAD

Bude to Meddon

In a roadside bank at Poughill [2192 0780] 2 m of stony Head rest on sandstone. At Grimscott [2715 0684] 1.5 m of grey yellow-weathering sandy clay lie on loose sandstone, and at Kingford [2880 0601] 1.8 m of orange, yellow and grey mottled sandy clay become very stony at depth.

A small stream [2177 1115] near Coombe shows 3 m of coarse stony Head. At Marsland [2177 1641] 1 m of yellow stony Head rests on shale. Near Welcombe a ditch [2296 1812] shows 2 m of stony sandy Head resting on sandstone.

A ditch [2654 1850] near Deptford exposes 2.5 m of extremely stony, yellow to orange-weathering silty clay; some of the sandstone debris is coated with ferruginous material and in places an iron oxide pan is developed. Near Gorvin 2 m of yellow silty stony Head overlie soft-weathering siltstone [2896 1975]. E C F

South Hole to Woolfardisworthy

Red-stained Head occurs near a fault [2206 2016] north of South Hole. At [2360 2105] an incised stream reveals 1.8 m of yellow silty clay Head with sandstone fragments. At [2623 2186] a ditch penetrates 1.2 m of stony Head with a yellow silty matrix.

The ground to the east of Bursdon and Welsford moors is generally poorly exposed. Drainage ditches in the forested areas and on poorly drained farmland reveal typical sections of yellow to buff silty clay with varied proportions of sandstone fragments. Ditches about 1 m deep, farther east on the northern part of Binworthy Moor are in yellow to buff silty clay with few sandstone fragments. In wetter areas peaty topsoil overlies mottled yellow and blue silty clay with sandstone fragments. On Welsford Moor [2750 2051] a stream is incised 1.5 m into yellow silty clay with sandstone fragments. North of Trew [2958 2109] 1.4 m of sandstone brash are exposed. At [3128 2193] a ditch is cut 0.9 m into yellow and grey stony clay, and at [3125 2135] ditches up to 1.8 m deep penetrate stony silty Head which is yellow at the top and grey in the bottom of the ditches. R T T

BLOWN SAND

There is a proven thickness of 4.5 m of sand in a borehole [2040 0707] at Crooklets car park; and on Bude golf course, where the old dunes have an amplitude of the order of 3 m, the total thickness is probably of the order of 10 m. Sand continues to be blown inland at the present day.

In the cliffs north and south of Bude, there is a well-defined layer of sandy topsoil, 0.6 m thick, resting on Head. It consists of sand mixed with clay, and clearly owes its presence to the sand blown over the tops of the cliffs. During storms not only sand, but small shale fragments also, are blown up from the beach. The 'sandyness' of this topsoil disappears within about 1 km of the coast. At or close to the Head/topsoil interface there is a horizon at which scattered flint fragments may be found. These are all chips and flakes, obviously exotic, and can be attributed to human action.

The true blown sand is composed predominantly of shell fragments, and has been used as a lime fertiliser in the past. This may explain the occurrence of beach pebbles found inland in ploughed fields; they are especially common near Northcott Mouth. E C F

ALLUVIUM

North-west area

A stream south of Binworthy Moor shows the following section [2870 2043]: yellow clay 0.3 m, overlain by gravel 0.15 to 0.3 m, yellow to buff silty clay 0.6 to 0.75 m and topsoil 0.3 m. This deposit is probably reworked Head resting on Head. In the Clifford Water [3029 2051] gravel and large sandstone fragments are overlain by 0.6 to 0.9 m of brown clay. The confluence of the Seckington and Clifford waters is marked by a broad spread of alluvium in which the stream [3002 2012] has exposed 1.0 to 1.3 m of yellow to buff stony and silty clay.   RTT

Welcombe Mouth to Duckpool

The following sections are visible: at [2196 1878] coarse cobble gravel 0.3 m overlain by brown silty clay with some gravel 1.0 m; at [2232 1892] 2.4 m of coarse brown gravel; at [2323 1723] gravel overlain by 2 m of stony clay Head; at [2395 1635] coarse gravel with a ferruginous cement beneath 0.75 m of brown sandy clay; at [2406 1376] clayey gravel with a ferruginous cement below 0.6 m of silty brown clay; at [2483 1315] gravelly clay with ferruginous cement and concretions overlain by 1.2 m of yellowish grey silty clay.

River Neet drainage

Sections include: at [2296 0983] 1 m brownish grey clay containing some pebbles; at [2459 0800] yellowish grey clay overlain by 0.6 m of brown peaty soil; at [2455 2805] a ferruginous-cemented pebble band within clay.

A large flat marshy area of alluvium [207 075] occurs north of Crooklets between Maer Farm and Maer Lodge. At its southern end it is covered by blown sand. Boreholes at Crooklets proved alluvial deposits beneath the blown sand. The boreholes also showed that at Crooklets car park bedrock is at a depth of 9.1 m. The blown sand in the car park was shown to range from 1.8 to 4.5 m in thickness. It overlies 1 to 2 m of grey silty sand, probably alluvial, which in turn overlies peat up to 2.7 m thick containing tree stumps. This submerged forest and peat bed extends out beneath the sea at Maer Lake. Thin peat beds also occur locally in the grey silty sand. The main peat bed overlies 0.9 to 1.8 m of clay which rest on Bude Formation strata. This clay, which contains sandstone fragments, is probably Head derived from weathering of the underlying rock. Buried valleys are postulated extending inland from Crooklets both north towards Maer Farm and east to Flexbury. They are narrow where they cross the sandstone ridge which forms Wrangle Point. The stream which now enters the sea at Crooklets appears too small to have excavated these valleys; this suggests a change in drainage pattern, though no obvious river capture has occurred.

Boreholes in the valley of the River Neet at Bude show that it too is an infilled drowned valley with bedrock hidden by a minimum depth of 12 m of silt, sand, gravel and pebbles.

River Tamar drainage

Sections include: at [2717 1508] clayey gravel with some sandstone fragments 0.38 m, overlain by clay with much organic material and some gravel 0.6 m; at [2848 1269] brown clay with yellow spots 0.1 m, overlain by brownish grey extremely silty clay 0.6 m and brown clay with a silty dark brown organic-rich layer at the base 0.45 m; at [2783 1729] yellow stony silty clay 0.15 m, overlain by gravel 0.15 m and brownish orange clay 0.45 m; at [2920 1861] 0.3 m of yellowish orange sandy clay with gravel overlain by 0.6 m of orange to brown silty clay; at [2946 1868] fairly coarse gravel 0.6 m, overlain by mottled greyish yellow sandy clay with some stones 0.45 m and brown soil rich in organic material 0.15 m; at [3094 1803] 0.3 m of coarse gravel overlain by 1.1 m of brown silty clay; at [3260 1770] 0.13 m of clayey gravel overlain by 1 m of brown silty clay; at [3394 1719] 0.8 m of coarse gravel lies beneath 0.2 m of brown silty clay.   ECF

River Torridge drainage

In the south-east of the district broad strips of alluvium (up to 400 m wide) are mainly confined to the stream from Cookbury Moor Plantation to the River Waldon, the River Waldon and the River Torridge. Exposed sections are generally few and nondescript, but include: at [3828 0677] 1.2 m of silt; at [3915 0653] 1 m of stony silt; at [4154 0801] 0.3 m of silty sand overlain by 1.2 m of silt; at [4213 0960] subrounded gravel overlain by 1 m of brown and grey silt; at [4238 0916] similar gravel below 1.3 m of silt; at [4298 0825] 4 m of stony silt; at [4613 0815] 0.2 m of gravel overlain by 0.4 m of stony silt; at [4777 0623] 0.5 m of gravel beneath 2.1 m of silt; at [4853 0591] 1 m of angular gravel overlain by 1 m of rusty brown silty sand with pebbles.   EAE

Downstream of Great Torrington the Torridge alluvial belt gradually widens to about 300 m at Weare Giffard. The following section was recorded at [4778 2157]: sandstone and shale overlain by angular sandstone gravel 0.55 m, grey silty clay with scattered sandstone pebbles 0.80 m, lenticular bed of subrounded sandstone gravel 0.10 m and reddish brown silty clay 0.75 m.   BJW

CHAPTER 6
Economic geology

MINING

Trials for copper have been reported at Alwington [405 232], south-west of Bideford (Vancouver, 1808), and at 'Hartland Mine' near Coalpit Lane, Hartland (Chope, 1902). However no traces of workings remain and although chalcopyrite mineralisation has been noted in faults on the Hartland coast it seems unlikely that any copper has been recovered (Edmonds, Williams and Taylor, 1979).

Mining of culm—seams of carbonaceous material within Upper Carboniferous rocks—used first as fuel and subsequently as a pigment, has been carried on (Figure 11) immediately north of the district intermittently from the Middle Ages until 1969 and is described elsewhere (Edmonds, Williams and Taylor, 1979).

Opencast working of pottery clays is taking place just east of the district (Freshney, Beer and Wright, 1979).

QUARRYING

Most of the small pits noted in Chapter 2 mark sites where stone, generally sandstone, has been dug for use in nearby buildings, roads and tracks. Many have supplied material for a single house or farm building.   EAE

The Braunton Sand Company's Beam Quarry [471 204], 3 km NW of Great Torrington, produces material for road-metal. A total thickness of about 28 m of Bude Formation sandstones and shales is worked, and the sandstones are crushed on-site.   BJW

At Colpit Quarry [2789 2492] 5.6 m of thinly and medium-bedded micaceous sandstones with subordinate shales and siltstones are similarly worked for roadmetal. Bradworthy Mill Quarry [3180 1435], the property of E.C.C. Quarries Ltd but not currently in use, is free from obstruction and readily accessible and could be brought into use on demand. About 21 m of fine-grained bedded sandstones are exposed.

In smaller pits, 3.5 m of massive sandstone are exposed near Dunsdon [301 083] and 8 m of fine-grained bedded sandstones with subordinate shales at West Hamsworthy [312 088]. A quarry [362 097] near Paddon Bridge contains 10 m of thickly bedded and massive sandstones with shale partings. Massive and thickly bedded feldspathic sandstones up to 7 m thick have been worked near Pitt, Shebbear [437 095], and 4 m of sandstones with subordinate shales south-east of Lovacott [461 080] and south of Buckland Mill [477 082]. Disused quarries in the neighbourhood of Sutcombe show 8 m of mainly thickly bedded sandstones [346 109] and 9 m of massive and thickly bedded sandstones [348 107]. Farther east a quarry [378 103] at Milton

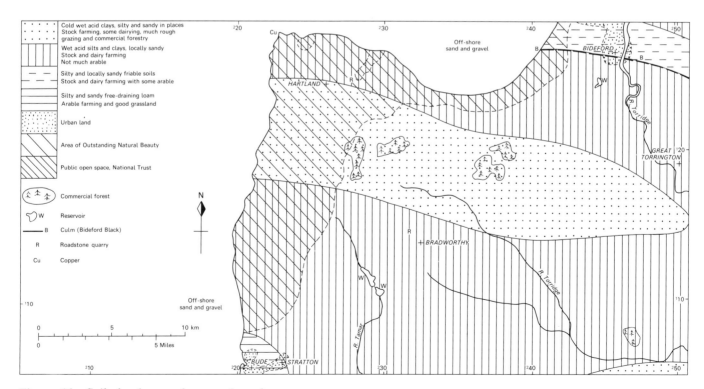

Figure 11 Soils, land use and economic geology

Mill has been opened in 5 m of thickly bedded sandstones with shaly partings, and another [391 102] south-west of Gratton shows 4.5 m of thickly bedded sandstones beneath 2.5 m of thin argillaceous beds.

SAND AND GRAVEL

Beach sand is available locally on the coast, particularly around Bude; it does not constitute a major resource and there are good amenity reasons for exploiting it very little or not at all. Some variably pebbly sand occurs nearby in the raised beach, just south of the district.

No workable gravels are known in the river terrace deposits, although patchy exposures occur (Chapter 5).

Off-shore deposits of sand and gravel are probably present in Bude Bay, but their extent is unknown, and there is no convenient harbour capable of handling large quantities, no great local demand and no suitable economic means of inland bulk transport.

SOILS AND LAND USE

Carboniferous rocks in the south-east of the district comprise interbedded groups of shales and sandstones generally reflected in the topography. Thus it is common to encounter damp silty clayey soils in the valleys whose naturally poor drainage is further hampered by developments of hard ferruginous and manganiferous 'pan' within a metre of the surface. Some sandy downwash from the slopes has occurred, and the ridges are capped by thin sandy and silty soils which are relatively free draining. Thus stock farming is common on the lower ground, with the incidence of dairy farming increasing on the slopes, and arable farming, although rarely dominant, commonest on the higher ground. More arable land occurs towards the coast at Bude, on the 60-m marine platform.

Farther north the underlying rocks are predominantly sandstones, but commonly fine-grained and silty and yielding fine-grained soils which readily become waterlogged on the lower ground. Stock and dairy farming predominate. On the highest ground a combination of poor thin silty acid soil and exposed situation has led to the development of commercial forests of the more resilient softwoods.

WATER SUPPLY

Even where the Carboniferous bedrock is predominantly sandstone, its texture is commonly fine-grained and permeability low. A few coarser sandstones in the Bude Formation, especially in the south and in the extreme north of the district, may permit steady intergranular movement of groundwater, but none constitutes more than a very minor aquifer.

Appreciable storage of groundwater beneath the district is likely to be confined to fissure systems which, because of their limited extent and slow replenishment, may not be capable of maintaining high yields to wells. However there is every likelihood of tapping supplies adequate for single houses or farms. Records of 82 wells and boreholes in the district, many less than 30 m deep and only one more than 60 m, show typical yields to be 1500 to 2500 litres per hour (l/h). The poorest results are around 900 l/h, and 11 boreholes yielded more than 4500 l/h. Of these, the maximum yield was from a 30-m borehole at Melbury water works which gave over 6000 l/h.

The only superficial deposits sufficiently thick to store considerable amounts of groundwater are the alluvial and river terrace flats of the River Torridge, the River Waldon, the tributary stream flowing east from Brendon and the Blagdonmoor Wharf area. But these drift deposits are unlikely to exceed 6 m in thickness, they contain much silt and clay with only pockets of gravel and they are invariably capped by silty clay which restricts infiltration. Hence they offer only small supplies, drawn from near the surface, in hydrological continuity with the river bed and subject to pollution.

Lower Tamar Lake, constructed to feed the northern branch of the Bude Canal, now supplies water to Bude and Stratton. It is a small reservoir covering an area of 20.7 ha and with a total capacity of 304 000 m³. A new dam nearby impounds 1 135 000 m³ of water covering 30.0 ha, Upper Tamar Lake.

All future large supplies of water drawn from within the district must be taken from surface water, either reservoirs or river intakes. The bedrock is commonly of low permeability, and numerous possible sites for small reservoirs exist. Storage on a medium scale, with man-made lakes several kilometres long, would be possible in the valleys of the Waldon and the Torridge. The only really large reservoir which could extend within the district would be that created by estuary storage in the River Torridge.

FUTURE PROSPECTS

Mineral resources are few, and there is no prospect of mining. Vast resources of Carboniferous sandstone are available for possible use in the construction industry but the pattern of past workings, with numerous small pits opened for strictly local purposes, may be projected into the future. Some roadwork may take place in the district, but no major construction projects are likely. Thus quarrying will not increase appreciably, since transport of stone beyond the district would be uneconomic. Similar difficulties would attend the exploitation of off-shore sand and gravel.

No major aquifer exists to serve the area. All large water supplies will be drawn directly from rivers or from reservoirs, possibly outside the present district.

The combination of geology and climate has resulted in little rich agricultural land, a good deal of medium-quality farmland suitable for stock-rearing and dairying, and some extensive tracts of poor wet acid soils in exposed positions. Striking increases in productivity are unlikely.

Inland landscapes are not such as to attract many holidaymakers but the coastline, of rugged cliffs, bays and rocky coves, with sandy beaches in the south, will continue to draw mainly small but steady numbers of discerning tourists.

The only change which might radically alter this projection of the present pattern would be new extensive urban development, with its attendant industry, communications, and demands for construction raw materials and power. But although the Bude district is one of those which could accommodate such development with minimum loss of useful land, social and political factors suggest that the possibility is remote. E A E

References

ARBER, E. A. N. 1907. On the Upper Carboniferous rocks of west Devon and north Cornwall. *Q. J. Geol. Soc. London*, Vol. 63, pp. 1–28.
— 1911. *The coast scenery of north Devon.* (London: Dent.)

ASHWIN, D. P. 1958. The coastal outcrop of the Culm Measures of south-west England. *Abstr. Proc. Conf. Geol. Geomorphol. South West Engl.*, Vol. 2, pp. 2–3.

BURNE, R. V. 1970. The origin and significance of sand volcanoes in the Bude Formation (Cornwall). *Sedimentology*, Vol. 15, pp. 211–228.
— and MOORE, L. J. 1971. The Upper Carboniferous rocks of Devon and north Cornwall. *Proc. Ussher Soc.*, Vol. 2, pp. 288–298.

CHOPE, R. P. 1902. Mining at Hartland. Notes of the past. No. 45. *Hartland Chron.*, No. 73, p. 30.

CONYBEARE, J. J. 1814. Memoranda relative to Clovelly, north Devon. *Trans. Geol. Soc. London*, Vol. 2. p. 498.
— 1823. On the geology of Devon and Cornwall. *Ann. Philos.*, Vol, 5, p. 184; Vol. 6, p. 35.

DEARMAN, W. R. 1963. Wrench faulting in Cornwall and south Devon. *Proc. Geol. Assoc.*, Vol. 74, pp. 265–287.
— 1967. Structural patterns in the Upper Carboniferous rocks at Welcombe Mouth, north Devon. *Trans. Devon. Assoc.*, Vol. 99, pp. 273–286.
— 1969. On the association of upright and recumbent folds on the southern margin of the Carboniferous synclinorium of Devonshire and north Cornwall. *Proc. Ussher Soc.*, Vol. 2, pp. 115–121.

DE LA BECHE, H. T. 1835. On the anthracite found near Bideford in north Devon. *Proc. Geol. Soc. London*, Vol. 2, p. 106.
— 1839. Report on the geology of Cornwall, Devon and west Somerset. *Mem. Geol. Surv. G.B.*

DE RAAF, J. F. M., READING, H. G. and WALKER, R. G. 1965. Cyclic sedimentation in the lower Westphalian of north Devon, England. *Sedimentology*, Vol. 4, pp. 1–52.

EDMONDS, E. A. 1972. The Pleistocene history of the Barnstaple area. *Rep. Inst. Geol. Sci.*, No. 72/2.
— 1974. Classification of the Carboniferous rocks of south-west England. *Rep. Inst. Geol. Sci.*, No. 74/13.
— McKEOWN, M. C. and WILLIAMS, M. 1975. South-west England. *Br. Reg. Geol., Inst. Geol. Sci.*
— WILLIAMS, B. J. and TAYLOR, R. T. 1979. Geology of Bideford and Lundy Island. *Mem. Geol. Surv. G.B.*, Sheet No. 292.
— WRIGHT, J. E., BEER, K. E., HAWKES, J. R., WILLIAMS, M., FRESHNEY, E. C. and FENNING, P. J. 1968. Geology of the country around Okehampton. *Mem. Geol. Surv. G.B.*, Sheet No. 324.

ETHERIDGE, R. 1867. On the physical structure of west Somerset and north Devon and on the palaeontological value of the Devonian rocks. *Q. J. Geol. Soc. London*, Vol. 23, pp. 568–698.

FRESHNEY, E. C., BEER, K. E. and WRIGHT, J. E. 1979. Geology of the country around Chulmleigh. *Mem. Geol. Surv. G.B.*, Sheet No. 309.
— McKEOWN, M. C. and WILLIAMS, M. 1972. Geology of the coast between Tintagel and Bude. *Mem. Geol. Surv. G.B.*, Sheet No. 322 (part of).
— and TAYLOR, R. T. 1971. The structure of mid-Devon and north Cornwall. *Proc. Ussher Soc.*, Vol. 2, pp. 241–248.
— — 1972. The Upper Carboniferous stratigraphy of north Cornwall and west Devon. *Proc. Ussher Soc.*, Vol. 2, pp. 464–471.

HAMLING, J. G. and ROGERS, I. 1910. Excursion to north Devon. *Proc. Geol. Assoc.*, Vol. 21, pp. 457–472.

HOUSE, M. R. and SELWOOD, E. B. 1966. Palaeozoic palaeontology in Devon and Cornwall. *In* Present views of some aspects of the geology of Cornwall and Devon. *R. Geol. Soc. Cornwall*, Commem. Vol. for 1964, pp. 45–86.

KING, A. F. 1965. Xiphosurid trails from the Upper Carboniferous of Bude, north Cornwall. *Proc. Geol. Soc. London*, No. 1626, pp. 162–165.
— 1966. Structure and stratigraphy of the Upper Carboniferous Bude Sandstones, north Cornwall. *Proc. Ussher Soc.*, Vol. 1, pp. 229–232.
— 1967. Stratigraphy and structure of the Upper Carboniferous Bude Formation, north Cornwall. Unpublished Ph.D. Thesis, University of Reading.
— 1971. Correlation in the Upper Carboniferous Bude Formation, north Cornwall. *Proc. Ussher Soc.*, Vol. 2, pp. 285–288.

LOVELL, J. P. B. 1965. The Bude Sandstones from Bude to Widemouth, north Cornwall. *Proc. Ussher Soc.*, Vol. 1, pp. 172–174.

MACKINTOSH, D. M. 1965. The tectonics of Namurian and Westphalian turbidite sandstones between Wanson Mouth and Rusey, north Cornwall. Unpublished Ph.D. Thesis, University of Exeter.

McKEOWN, M. C., EDMONDS, E. A., WILLIAMS, M., FRESHNEY, E.C. and SMITH, D. J. MASSON. 1973. Geology of the country around Boscastle and Holsworthy. *Mem. Geol. Surv. G.B.*, Sheet Nos. 322 and 323.

PRENTICE, J. E. 1960. The stratigraphy of the Upper Carboniferous rocks of the Bideford region, north Devon. *Q. J. Geol. Soc. London*, Vol. 116, pp. 397–408.

RAMSBOTTOM, W. H. C. 1970. Some British Carboniferous goniatites of the Family Anthracoceratidae. *Bull. Geol. Surv. G.B.*, No. 32, pp. 53–60.

READING, H. G. 1965. Recent finds in the Upper Carboniferous of south-west England and their significance. *Nature, London*, Vol. 208, pp. 745–748.

ROGERS, I. 1907. On fossil fish. *Trans. Devon. Assoc.*, Vol. 39, pp. 394–398.
— 1908. On the submerged forest at Westward Ho! A history of Northam Burrows. *Trans. Devon. Assoc.*, Vol. 40, pp. 249–259.
— 1909. On a further discovery of fossil fish and mollusca in the Upper Culm Measures of north Devon. *Trans. Devon. Assoc.*, Vol. 41, pp. 309–319.
— 1910. A synopsis of the fossil flora and fauna of the Upper Culm Measures of north-west Devon. *Trans. Devon. Assoc.*, Vol. 42, pp. 538–564.

SANDERSON, D. J. 1974. Chevron folding in the Upper Carboniferous rocks of north Cornwall. *Proc. Ussher Soc.*, Vol. 3, pp. 96–103.

SEDGWICK, A. and MURCHISON, R. I. 1840. On the physical structure of Devonshire, and on the subdivisions and geological relations of its older stratified deposits. *Trans. Geol. Soc. London*, Vol. 5, pp. 633–705.

SELWOOD, E. B., EDWARDS, R. A., SIMPSON, S., CHESHER, J. A., HAMBLIN, R. J. O., HENSON, M. R., RIDDOLLS, B. W. and WATERS, R. A. In preparation. Geology of the country around Newton Abbot. 2nd Ed. *Mem. Geol. Surv. G.B.*, Sheet No. 339.

USSHER, W. A. E. 1881. On the Palaeozoic rocks of north Devon and west Somerset. *Geol. Mag.*, Vol. 8, pp. 441–448.
— 1887. The Culm of Devonshire. *Geol. Mag.*, Vol. 24, pp. 10–117.

56 REFERENCES

— 1892.   The British Culm Measures.   *Proc. Somerset Archaeol. Nat. Hist. Soc.*, Vol. 38, pp. 111–219.

— 1900.   The Devonian, Carboniferous and New Red rocks of west Somerset, Devon and Cornwall.   *Proc. Somerset Archaeol. Nat. Hist. Soc.*, Vol. 46, pp. 1–64.

— 1901.   The Culm-Measure types of Great Britain.   *Trans. Inst. Min. Eng.*, Vol. 20, pp. 360–391.

— 1906.   *Victoria History of the Counties of England: Devonshire.* (London.)

VANCOUVER, C. 1808.   *General view of the agriculture of the county of Devon.*   (London.)

WHITTAKER, A. 1975.   A postulated post-Hercynian rift valley system in southern Britain.   *Geol. Mag.*, Vol. 112, pp. 137–149.

APPENDIX 1

List of principal fossil localities and faunas collected during the survey

Fossil determinations are by Dr M. A. Calver and Dr W. H. C. Ramsbottom. The registered numbers of specimens are followed by the fossil lists to which they refer. Specimens are stored in the Leeds office of the Institute of Geological Sciences.

Namurian fauna (G₁)

Skittering Rock Shale

1 Skittering Rock [3174 2508]. DEB 7266–73. *Dunbarella sp.*, *?Gastrioceras cancellatum* Bisat.

Westphalian faunas (G₂)

Embury Shale

2 Cliff [2155 1981]. DEB 7387–91; CF 625. *Gastrioceras subcrenatum* (Frech), *G. sp. nov. 1, G. sp. nov. 2.*
3 Reef on foreshore [2151 1977]. DEB 7373–86. *Gastrioceras sp. nov. 1, G. sp. nov. 2.*
4 Base of cliff [2159 1974]. DEB 7277–93; CL 90–8. *Gastrioceras subcrenatum, G. sp. nov. 1, G. sp. nov. 2.*
5 Colpit (Hescott) Quarry [2789 2492]. CL 52–63; 192–9. *Gastrioceras* cf. *subcrenatum, G. sp. nov.*

Gull Rock Shale

6 Base of cliff in north wall of promontory north of Shag Rock [2135 1903]. KEB 84–8; DEB 7252–65. *Gastrioceras circumnodosum* Foord, *G. coronatum* (Foord & Crick), *G. listeri* (J. Sowerby).
7 Stream [2491 1735]. CF 637. *Gastrioceras listeri.*
8 Scree at base of cliff, Gull Rock Beach [2149 1999]. DEB 7299–330. *Annularia sp., Dunbarella sp., Gastrioceras circumnodosum.* CL 102–3. *Rhabdoderma sp.* [2140 2001]. DEB 7331–72; CL 100–1. *Gastrioceras circumnodosum, G. listeri, Homoceratoides* aff. *divaricatus* (Hind).
9 Elmscott Gutter [2228 2159]. DEB 6899–940. Carbonised wood, *Anthracoceratites sp., Gastrioceras circumnodosum, G. listeri.* WJ 152–63. *G. circumnodosum.*
10 Tosberry Moor [2568 2122]. CL 123–36, *Anthracoceratites sp., Gastrioceras circumnodosum, G. listeri.* [2620 2106]. CL 137–51, loose in stream bed. *Dunbarella sp., Gastrioceras listeri.*
11 Docton Farm [2462 2139]. CL 152–167. Anthracoceratids, *Gastrioceras* cf. *circumnodosum.*
12 Hartland Mill [2486 2456]. CL 1–6. *Gastrioceras circumnodosum.* [2483 2459]. CL 7–8. *Gastrioceras sp.* [2476 2480]. CL 9–11. *Gastrioceras sp.* [2463 2478]. CL 12–13. *Rhabdoderma elegans* Newberry.

Hartland Quay Shale

13 Reef on foreshore [2067 1697]. DEA 320–31. Indet. goniatites, conodonts including *Hindeodella*, ostracods (*Paraparchites?*), fish fragments. DEA 332–54 (2 m above DEA 320–31). *Caneyella sp.*, anthracoceratids.

14 Sandhole Rock [2184 2077]. DEB 7294–8; CL 104–6. *Gastrioceras* cf. *amaliae* Schmidt. [2175 2081]. CL 107. *Anthracoceratites sp.* [2194 2093]. DEB 6879–94. *Caneyella sp.*, turreted gastropods, *Anthracoceratites sp., ?G. amaliae*, mollusc spat. [2192 2094]. WJ 149. *?G. amaliae.*
15 Hole Rock [2229 2261]. CL 207–9. Anthracoceratids, *Gastrioceras* cf. *amaliae*, conodonts including *Hindeodella sp.* [2218 2262]. CL 210–1, *G.* cf. *amaliae.* [2215 2262]. CL 14–6. *Anthracoceratites sp.*, juvenile goniatites and spat.
16 Speke's Mill Beach [2263 2375]. CL 108–13. *Anthracoceratites sp., Gastrioceras amaliae*, conodonts.
17 Hartland Quay [2242 2485]. DEB 7419–23; CL 117–8. *Posidonia?*, anthracoceratids. [2251 2487]. CL 114–6. Anthracoceratids.

Longpeak Shale

18 Reef on foreshore [2059 1691]. DEA 299–319. ?Goniatite spat, coprolites, fish scale.
19 Longpeak Beach [2219 2268]. DEB 7424–8. Wood, *Caneyella?*, mollusc spat, fish? [2228 2271]. DEB 7392–7. *Calamites sp., Caneyella sp.*, juvenile goniatites, coprolite pellets. [2229 2272]. DEB 7398–411. *Caneyella sp.*, mollusc spat, fish remains including an acanthodian spine.
20 Longpeak [2213 2303]. DEB 7412–8. *Caneyella sp.*, fish remains.
21 Base of cliff 550 m E of Lily Rock [3416 2384]. DEB 7197–211. *Caneyella sp.*, goniatite spat. ?Longpeak Shale.

Saturday's Pit Shale

22 Base of cliff [2026 0694]. DEB 6435–60. Eurypterid?, fish remains including *Acanthodes wardi* Egerton, *Cornuboniscus budensis* White, palaeoniscid scales.
23 North-east corner of swimming pool [2027 0682]. DEB 6393–434. Eurypterid?, fish remains including *Cornuboniscus budensis*, acanthodian indet.

Sandy Mouth Shale

24 Cliff [1999 1334]. DEB 6497–561; CF 636. *Caneyella sp.* [juv.], *Dunbarella sp., Anthracoceratoides cornubiensis* Ramsbottom, palaeoniscid scales.
25 Reef on foreshore [1968 1290]. DEB 6562–70. *Anthracoceratoides cornubiensis*, fish remains including palaeoniscid scales.
26 Cliff [1967 1287]. DEB 6571–97. *Caneyella sp., Dunbarella sp., Anthracoceratoides cornubiensis.*
27 Foreshore [2011 1000] opposite steps at entrance to beach at Sandy Mouth. HR 2156–69; WT 86–7. *Caneyella sp., Anthracoceratoides cornubiensis.*
28 Loose material in stream bed [2672 1151]. CF 627–8. *Anthracoceratites sp.* (?Sandy Mouth Shale).

Warren Gutter Shale

29 Reef on foreshore [2005 1108]. DEB 6640–56. Fish including *Rhabdoderma sp.*, palaeoniscid scales.
30 Nodular band in cliff [2013 1099]. MC 491–546. *Caneyella sp., Dunbarella macgregori* (Currie), *'Anthracoceras' hindi* Bisat, *Gastrioceras depressum* Delépine, orthocone nautiloid.

APPENDIX 2

List of Geological Survey Photographs

Copies of these photographs may be seen in the library of the Institute of Geological Sciences, Exhibition Road, South Kensington, London SW7 2DE. Prints and lantern slides may be purchased. Photographs with numbers up to 5939 were taken by Mr J. Rhodes and are available in black and white only. Those with higher numbers were taken by Mr C. Jeffery and are available in colour and black and white. The photographs belong to Series A.

CARBONIFEROUS

Crackington Formation

5910–1	Waterfall in Milford Water, above Speke's Mill Mouth.
5912	Folded strata and foreshore reefs near Speke's Mill Mouth.
5913	Folded strata eroded by river and sea, St Catherine's Tor, Hartland Quay.
5914–5	Foreshore reefs and collapsed strata in cliffs just south of Hartland Quay.
5916	Reefs of folded strata just north of Hartland Quay.
5917–8	Zigzag and 'S'-shaped folds north of Hartland Quay.
5919–20	Folded strata north of Hartland Quay.
11593	Upright chevron folds, Warren Beach, Hartland Quay [2230 2479].
11594	Flute-casts on sandstone, shore below St Catherine's Tor, Hartland Quay [2240 2410].
11595	Steeply dipping strata with waterfall, Speke's Mill Mouth [2252 2358].
12042	Zigzag folds, Gunpath Beach [2220 2240]. (Plate 8).
12043	Folds, Nabor Point [2145 2020].
12044	Anticline, Elmscott Gutter [2227 2162]. (Plate 9).
12045	Folds, Warren Cliff [2255 2506].
12046	Zigzag folds, Warren Cliff [2255 2496].
12047	Folds, Warren Cliff [2245 2520].
12052	Folds, Broadbench Cove [216 197].
12053	Basal Westphalian strata, Embury Beacon [2160 1950].
12054	Folds, Embury Beacon [216 194].
12465	Upright and recumbent folding, Welcombe Mouth [2124 1797].
12466	Shingle beach and Crackington Formation, Welcombe Mouth [2124 1797].
12467	Crumpled shales with thin sandstones, Embury Beach [2150 1956]. (Plate 2).
12468	Folded sandstones and shales, Embury Beach [2150 1956].
12469	Minor folds in shales and thin sandstones, north of Embury Beach [2157 1978].

Bude Formation

5887–8	Folded strata, Compass Point, Bude.
5889–95	Folded strata near the breakwater, Bude harbour.
5896	North-dipping sandstones and shales just north of Bude harbour.
5897–900	Folded strata near Wrangle Point, Bude.
5901–3	Vertical and folded strata near Maer Cliff.

5904–6	Vertical strata and asymmetric folds, Sandy Mouth.
5907–9	Folded strata, Northcott Mouth.
5929–30	Folded strata near Peppercombe Mouth.
11588	Pericline, Buck's Mills [3550 2367].
12041	Zigzag folds, Longpeak Beach [2228 2285].
12055	Syncline and anticline, Yeol Mouth [204 164].
12056	Anticline and syncline, Henna Cliff [2000 1583]. (Plate 7).
12057	Sandstones and slumped bed, Higher Sharpnose Point [195 148].
12058	Steeply dipping sandstones and shales, south of Higher Sharpnose Point [1970 1416].
12059	Box fold, Menachurch Point [2002 0880].
12060	Angular fold and box fold, Dunsmouth [2020 0938].
12061	Folds, Sandy Mouth [2015 1025].
12062	Folds, Warren Gutter [2007 1100].
12063	Folds, Lower Sharpnose Point [1970 1255].
12064	Gentle anticline with slumped bed, Steeple Point, Duckpool [1990 1165].
12065	Box fold, Dunsmouth [2013 0911]. (Plate 1).
12453	Nodular shale, Sandy Mouth [202 100].
12454–5	Sandstones and shales, Sandy Mouth [202 100].
12456	Slumped bed north of Sandy Mouth [2014 1044]. (Plate 6).
12457	Finely banded shales, siltstones and sandstones, Warren Gutter [201 110].
12458	Folds at Warren Gutter [201 110]. (Plate 3).
12459	Shales and sandstones, Oldwalls, Morwenstow [1975 1403].
12460	Cross-bedded sandstone, Oldwalls, Morwenstow [1975 1403]. (Plate 5).
12492	Sandstones and shales, Oldwalls, Morwenstow [1975 1403].
12493	Saturday's Pit Shale, west-north-west of Morwenstow [1995 1612].
12494	Sandstones, shales and mudstones, Yeol Mouth [2020 1628].
12495	Wedge-bedded sandstone, Yeol Mouth [2020 1628].
12496	Sandstone and slumped bed, Yeol Mouth [2020 1628].
12461, 12464, & 12499	Strata near the Crackington Formation–Bude Formation junction, Litter Mouth [2074 1694].
12462	Wedge-bedded sandstone, Yeol Mouth [2020 1628]. (Plate 4).
12463	Steeply dipping sandstones and shales, Yeol Mouth [2020 1628].
12470	Sandstones in Northcott Park Quarry, north of Stratton [2320 0895].
12480–1	Sandstones with shales, Pigsdon Quarry [2766 0936].
12489–91	Sandstones and shales, Beam Quarry [471 204].

PERMIAN

5926–8	Breccia, Portledge Mouth.
11589–90	Breccia, Portledge Mouth [3860 2463].

TOPOGRAPHY

5936–7	Valley of River Yeo near Landcross.
5938	River cliff, River Torridge, near Weare Giffard.
5939	Valley of River Torridge south of Bideford.
11591	Dissected and abandoned valley, Screda Point, Hartland Quay [2230 2470].

11592	Coastal scenery of folded Crackington Formation strata, Warren Cliff, Hartland Quay [2230 2479].
11596	Dissected and abandoned valley, St Catherine's Tor, Hartland Quay [2260 2435].
11597	Inland scenery, Crackington Formation, Hartland [2885 2467].
12471–2	River terrace scenery east of Duckpool [204 115].
12473–4	Crackington Formation landscape south of Gorvin Cross [2968 1900].
12475	Bude Formation landscape south-west of Woolley Barrows [2605 1642].
12476–7	Tamar Lake reservoir [2947 1080].
12478–9	River terrace scenery, River Tamar east of Stratton [2793 0620].
12482–3	River Torridge valley south of Ashmansworthy [3394 1720].

INDEX

HER MAJESTY'S STATIONERY OFFICE

Government Bookshops
49 High Holborn, London WC1V 6HB
13a Castle Street, Edinburgh EH2 3AR
41 The Hayes, Cardiff CF1 1JW
Brazennose Street, Manchester M60 8AS
Southey House, Wine Street, Bristol BS1 2BQ
258 Broad Street, Birmingham B1 2HE
80 Chichester Street, Belfast BT1 4JY
Government publications are also available through booksellers

INSTITUTE OF GEOLOGICAL SCIENCES
Exhibition Road, London SW7 2DE

Murchison House, West Mains Road,
Edinburgh EH9 3LA

The full range of Institute publications is
displayed and sold at Murchison House and at
the Institute's Bookshop at the Geological
Museum, Exhibition Road, London SW7 2DE

*The Institute was formed by the incorporation of
the Geological Survey of Great Britain and the Geological
Museum with Overseas Geological Surveys and is a
constituent body of the Natural Environment
Research Council.*